Making & Modifying
Woodworking Tools

Making & Modifying
Woodworking
Tools

Jim Kingshott

Guild of Master Craftsman Publications Ltd

First Published in 1992 by
Guild of Master Craftsman Publications Ltd,
Castle Place, 166 High Street,
Lewes, East Sussex BN7 1XU

Reprinted 1993

ISBN 0 946 819 32 7

Designed by Fineline Studios

Printed and bound in Great Britain by
Redwood Books, Trowbridge, Wiltshire

To my son John, whose untimely death
brought this book into being.

Contents

Introduction

Whenever I am visited in my workshop by a fellow woodworker, the conversation nearly always comes round to the making of tools. It usually starts with the visitor politely asking how an ordinary craftsman can afford such tools. There is no mystery to this: I have made most of them myself. Many of my friends have seen my efforts and followed suit; I hope the reader will – by reading this book – be able to do the same.

There are one or two points I would like to make that will help in using the book. First, the projects included are ranged across the skills required to make tools. Each project adds to the skill learnt from the previous items, so it would be unwise to open the book at a particular tool and attempt to make it without reference to what has gone before. Consequently, I would counsel the would-be toolmaker to read the book from cover to cover before attempting to make any of the tools.

In making the drawings and describing the tools I had to make a decision as to which system of measurement to use. As the tools are all of a period pre-decimalisation, and so am I, imperial measurement is used throughout. There is a conversion table at the back of the book, should you require it.

I would like to take this opportunity to wish the reader many satisfying hours using the tools they have made themselves.

Why Make or Modify a Tool?

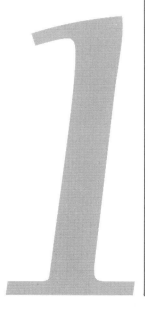

THE 'NOT SO GOOD' NEW TOOL

When we have paid out our money and got over the first thrill of using a new tool, if we are honest with ourselves we often come to realise that this tool could be better. Because of the constraints put upon manufacturers financially and by mass production methods of construction, they use a lot of cost engineering. By this I mean that they search for alterations to the design that will save time and materials and look for modifications to the design that will make the tool easier to produce with their machinery.

This of course means that the production costs come down and the item produced can then compete in the marketplace with a better chance of success. High volume sales are important with the production methods of today because of the great cost of original tooling for sophisticated, computer-controlled machines.

These methods have reduced prices, but have also unfortunately reduced the quality. This might not matter so much to the DIY user, who is the buyer that most woodworking tools are now aimed for. However, to the serious woodworker wanting to produce high quality work, the lack of the finest tools can be a serious drawback.

WHERE HAVE ALL THE GOOD TOOLS GONE?

Not only is there a lack of quality new tools, but the price of good secondhand tools has risen beyond the reach of most craftsmen. This is due to the rise in the number of people who have started collecting tools, which has caused demand to outstrip supply. Most of these collectors do not put the tools to use, but just want to build a collection – a worthy intention when there is a good historic reason for preserving a tool, but unfortunately every

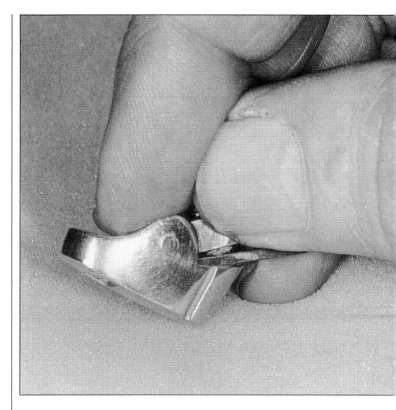

Fig 1.1 Any size plane can be made – this baby violin plane fits on the end of the index finger.

tool collected is another tool removed from the craftsman's bench.

Many collectors are interested only in the finest tools, and of course these are just the tools that the hand woodworker needs. Top auction houses now hold regular sales, and some very fine tools come under the hammer. Unfortunately for the craftsman, the price realised is usually well beyond his reach.

Not long ago there were stallholders in most markets who sold secondhand tools, but most of these have now disappeared and they are unable to replenish their stocks with suitable items. Where they do exist, most have put up their prices to reflect the price tools fetch at auction.

There is that recent trend, the car boot sale; very occasionally a bargain can be found, but my experience is that as a rule the proprietors have an enhanced notion of the value. Because they do not understand the tools they seem to think that all old woodworking tools can be classed in the same category, and thus ask much more than the item is worth. Added to this, many secondhand tools they offer have not been looked after and require a good deal of work to put them back into a condition where they can again grace a craftsman's bench.

SPECIAL TOOLS

There is also the situation where a craftsman who has a particular way of working sees the need for a special tool that has never been produced by a manufacturer (*see* Fig 1.1). In the early part of this century the Stanley Rule and Level Company included a little notice in the box that every tool was packed in, addressed to the purchaser and stating that if there was any modification that could be suggested to improve the tool's performance, Stanley would consider adopting it – if adopted they would pay for the suggestion.

This was not all: the notice went on to say that if the purchaser suggested a design for a tool that was not already being manufactured, Stanley would be interested. Sadly, today there is no such facility.

If we see the need for a special tool, there are only three alternative ways that the problem can be approached: make it yourself, get somebody to make it for you, or manage without it. The third is a choice unacceptable to any self-respecting craftsman, and for that reason is not worth considering.

The time involved in making a one-off tool, unless it is of very simple design, or you have some very good and obliging friends, is going to cost money. That only leaves the first alternative, a Hobson's choice if ever there was one.

PRIDE IN OWNERSHIP

There is yet another reason for making or modifying a tool – whether it is a good reason I am not sure, but it is one that I am personally guilty of. Pride in possession is probably the term that sums it up best, but I think that it goes much deeper than this.

A craftsman who wishes to produce the very finest work that it is possible to produce, has to psych himself up to this level. I find that having the very best tools available helps a long way towards this end. I know the old saying that, 'Only a poor workman blames his tools', but I think that whoever invented that was no craftsman.

There is nothing more frustrating than trying to cope with a tool that does not perform as you know it could or should. Most of us try to do something about it when we find ourselves in this situation, and that is how I first started, by modifying tools so they would perform better and then, when the tool was not capable of further improvement, by making my own, incorporating all I had learnt from carrying out the modifications (*see* Fig 1.2).

IDENTIFYING THE NEED TO MODIFY OR MAKE

Having used a tool for a time, it should be possible to decide where it falls short of the ideal. By making a conscious effort to note all its weak points, and writing them down so that a list is compiled, a specification for the criteria of a new tool that could replace the old one can be drawn up.

Fig 1.2 Set of violin planes machined from solid brass.

Fig 1.3 Standard marking gauge.

Keeping the new specification in mind, use the inferior tool again, to make sure that all its faults have been noted. Now, having looked at the faults and made a list, we need to decide how they will be overcome – but are there any other features that could be incorporated in the new tool that will improve its performance?

This period of analysing and appraisal should not be hurried. There is nothing worse than putting a lot of work into making a tool and then finding that it still falls short of what you wanted. So, armed with the specification that we have drawn up for our ideal tool, we can inspect the tool we have been using. Is it capable of modification? If not, we must now design a new one.

Over the years there have been many versions made of most woodworking tools, and these are worth studying, even if pictures in a book are all that is available. Visiting auction sales armed with a camera or sketchbook and a rule is useful, and illustrated auctioneers' catalogues can be a good source of ideas.

In later chapters of this book you will find details of tools that I have made. Each one was researched in some depth before any attempt was made to construct it, but even so, some of the tools are third-generation, where I did not get it right the first time. So be warned – an hour's thought at the start can save a week of work later.

Having seen what has been made in the past, analyse each item critically: see what features you would like to include in your design, and look to see how the faults you found in your original tool have been overcome. After this preliminary work you should have a good idea of what you want and how to achieve it.

DESIGNING

It is most important that proper accurate workshop drawings are prepared. Sketch your ideas down in rough to start with and refine them, incorporating changes as they occur to you. When the design seems incapable of further improvement, make full-size drawings. You may find that things will not work out the way you envisaged them in your original sketches – not to worry, this is part of the design process, and all the problems must be ironed out on paper.

The old adage 'make haste slowly' is very appropriate in this circumstance. I find it a good policy to put my design away for a couple of weeks; when I look at it again I invariably see things that were missed out or alterations that had not occurred to me before. I cannot stress too strongly that if the tool produced is to be worth the effort of manufacture, a lot of time and thought must go into this designing and refining process.

AN EXAMPLE

To show the technique of identifying the need for a special tool and the method of designing and making it, I will explain how my precision marking gauge came into being. The ordinary marking gauge made from hardwood (usually beech, but in some superior quality examples rosewood) is a tool that has been around in its present form for several hundred years – because of this, and its unchanged design (apart from the introduction of a plastic screw to replace the boxwood one), it must be efficient.

Over the years many variations have appeared on the market, and they are all worth looking at. On examination the basic design

Fig 1.4 (right) English double-stemmed metal marking and cutting gauge in steel and bronze.

Fig 1.5 Stanley metal marking gauge, cast iron head with steel stem.

is very similar: the stock with a hole near its centre through which the stem runs, with some form of screw or wedge to secure

Fig 1.6 (above) Selection of gauges showing how different makers have approached the tool.

Fig 1.7 German wooden double-stemmed marking gauge.

the stem in its set position in the stock (*see* Fig 1.3).

Among the variations, gauges with two or more stems are common (*see* Fig 1.4). Sometimes the whole tool is made from metal – bronze, brass, steel and cast iron – and on some the marking pin has been replaced by a sharp-edged wheel (*see* Figs 1.5 and 1.6). You

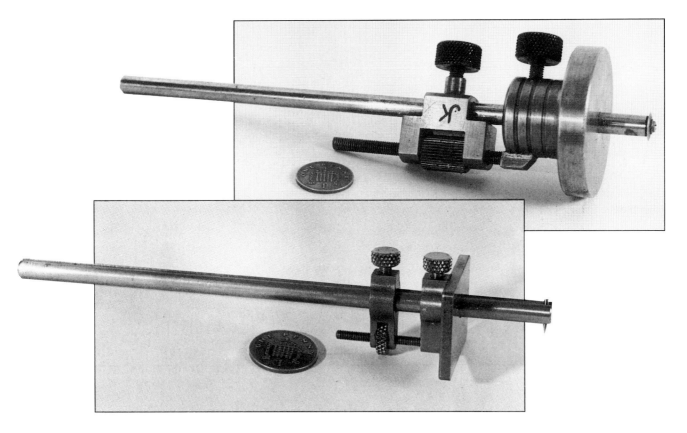

Fig 1.8 *(top) My own Mark I – a bit too heavy.*

Fig 1.9 *(below) Mark II – in use for 10 years.*

will see that over the years quite a few different designs have been produced: even wooden variants have appeared from time to time, some of a very superior design to the basic gauge (*see* Fig 1.7).

Most of these gauges can be bought for a reasonably small sum of money, unlike planes and similar tools. So why go to all the trouble of making a gauge at all? I like to work very precisely when I make a piece of furniture, and it has always annoyed me to have to keep tapping the end of the gauge stem on the bench to adjust the position of the stock. Although this method can position the stock with some accuracy, it always seemed to me that there must be a better way.

I often use an engineers' vernier calliper, and the way the jaws are adjusted gave me the idea that something like this could be fitted on to a marking gauge. I designed and made the Mark I, shown in Fig 1.8, which worked quite

well but was heavy, as it was turned up from solid brass. Though I used this gauge for a couple of years, I never was really happy with it and determined to make a better one when I had the time.

I went through the procedure previously mentioned, making a detailed list of the features that the new design would encompass. Many sketches were made, and eventually the Mark II was produced – this new version is exactly what I wanted, and after 10 years of daily use it has become the ideal tool (*see* Fig 1.9).

There are details of the construction and manufacture of the Mark I and II in Chapter 18. As every craftsman will have his own methods and ideals when working, and the same design of tool will not suit us all, some modifications will have to be made if we are to be happy with the tools that we use.

The average woodworker is a very adaptable being, and most can make or modify tools to their own requirements with some guidance, which I hope you will find in the following chapters of this book.

Materials & Finishes

WHY ?

The purpose of this book is to enable woodworkers to make tools, and for that reason I do not want to get bogged down in metallurgy. But it is important to know something of the materials that are to be used if our efforts are to be successful. Most of us have a limited budget, and will probably be looking for odds and ends of metal that are usable – the major problem with this approach is identifying the particular type of metal when we come across a piece that looks useful. It is therefore important that we are aware of the character of the more common metals that we will wish to use; this will help in deciding whether or not they are suitable for the job we have in mind.

Before looking at any individual metal, it is vital that certain properties which the material may or may not have are understood and defined. This will lead to a better understanding of explanations in later chapters, as well as the descriptions of the different metals given here.

STRENGTH

The strength of a metal is its ability to withstand stress without breaking. By stress I mean loads that may tend to stretch, compress, shear or twist. The forces that induce these stresses are known as tensile, compressive, shear and torsional. Some materials withstand one force better than others: for instance, cast iron has good compressive strength but poor tensile strength – it is about four times stronger when squeezed than when stretched. High strength will not be needed in a lot of the applications that we will want to put metal to, but other features will also be important, and could make the difference between a good and an average tool.

ELASTICITY AND PLASTICITY

Elasticity describes the ability of a material that is deformed from its original shape by a force to return to that original shape once the force is removed. A good example of this is spring steel. Most materials have some elasticity, but if a stress alters their shape beyond a certain limit they are permanently deformed. The point where this happens is known, as you would expect, as their elastic limit.

Plasticity is the opposite of elasticity, and describes the ability of a material to retain any deformation produced by a force after the force is removed. Some metals become plastic when their temperature is raised to red heat.

DUCTILITY AND MALLEABILITY

Ductile is the term applied to a material that can be easily formed to shape, often taking it well beyond its elastic limit without it breaking. An example of this would be the materials used in drawing wire: the wire is pulled through progressively smaller dies, making it smaller in diameter but longer in length.

Malleability is somewhat similar to the ductile property of a material, the difference being that the material is deformed by compressive forces such as hammering or rolling, instead of a tensile force. Lead is a good example of a malleable material, as it has very low tensile strength. One only has to see some of the beautiful work done by plumbers on lead rainwater fittings to appreciate how this material can be formed by beating it with a bossing mallet.

HARDNESS AND SOFTNESS

A *hard* metal is one that will resist wear, abrasion, scratching and penetration. There is a scientific way of measuring this characteristic, which is described in Chapter 6.

Softness, of course, is the opposite property to hardness. A soft metal can be worked easily, and is to be preferred where the attributes of hardness are not needed. As woodworkers, we are interested in the properties of some steels that enable them to be heat-treated to make them hard and capable of being sharpened, while retaining their cutting edge. Unfortunately, the harder steels are made, the more brittle they become.

BRITTLENESS AND TOUGHNESS

Brittleness describes the way a material will fracture before any, or very little, deformation occurs. An example of a brittle material is glass. For our cutting blade we must therefore make a compromise between hardness (which will be brittle) and toughness.

Toughness is the ability of the metal to withstand shock loads. A plane blade that was made too hard could easily be chipped when planing a pine board if there was a hard knot, so some toughness is desirable.

FUSIBILITY

All metals are fusible, i.e. they can be melted. The ones that melt at a low temperature are termed easily fusible, and those that require a high melt temperature are called refractory.

FERROUS AND NONFERROUS

Metals that contain iron are known as ferrous, so nonferrous metals are obviously those that have no iron in their make-up. Very rarely is a metal used in its pure state – most times it will be combined with other minerals to form an alloy.

Carbon is a most important additive to iron, as even in small quantities it causes large changes to the properties of that metal. All the steel you will use will be an alloy, as will be

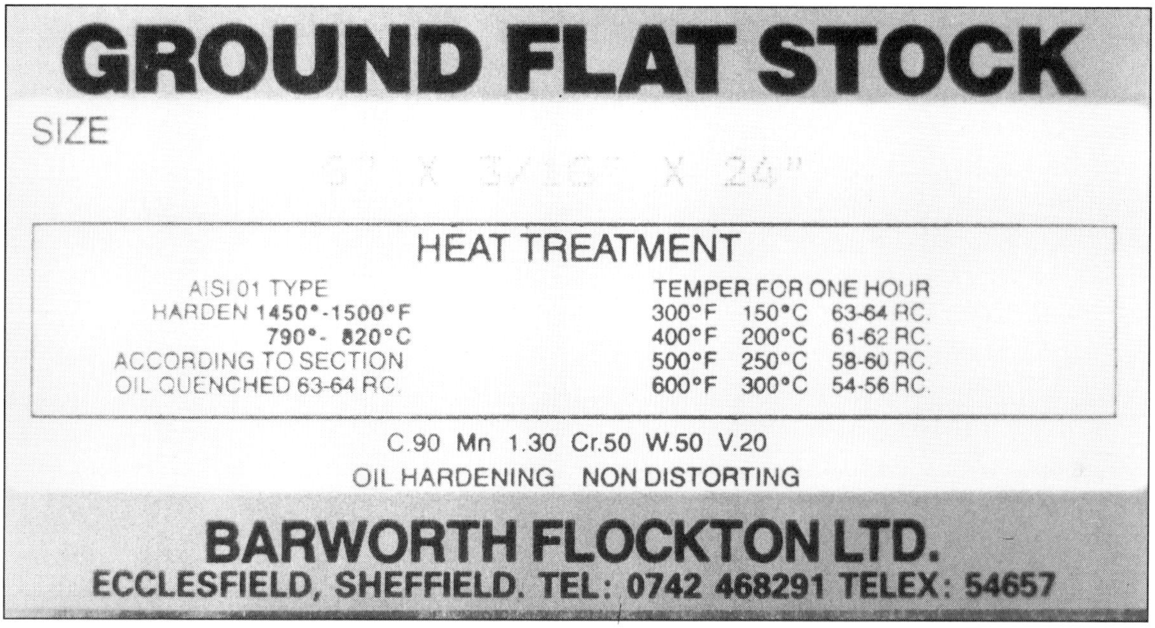

GROUND FLAT STOCK

SIZE
~~~ X 3/16" X 24"~~~

HEAT TREATMENT

AISI 01 TYPE	TEMPER FOR ONE HOUR
HARDEN 1450°-1500°F	300°F 150°C 63-64 RC.
790°- 820°C	400°F 200°C 61-62 RC.
ACCORDING TO SECTION	500°F 250°C 58-60 RC.
OIL QUENCHED 63-64 RC.	600°F 300°C 54-56 RC.

C.90 Mn 1.30 Cr.50 W.50 V.20
OIL HARDENING   NON DISTORTING

BARWORTH FLOCKTON LTD.
ECCLESFIELD, SHEFFIELD. TEL: 0742 468291 TELEX: 54657

Fig 2.1 Label from packet of ground plate tool steel. Note heat treatment instructions and composition: C = carbon, Mn = manganese, Cr = chromium, W = tungsten, V = vanadium.

nearly all the nonferrous metals (see Fig 2.1).

Having defined most of the terms that will be used when describing the different metals (any other definitions will be explained as they are used), let us now look at the individual materials and their properties.

INDUSTRIAL FERROUS METALS

PIG IRON

Pig iron is obtained by charging a blast furnace with iron ore, coke and limestone. The charge gradually sinks down to the bottom of the furnace, and the limestone and the impurities from the ore form a fusible slag, which floats on top of the molten metal and is blown off at intervals.

The furnace is tapped and the molten metal run off into pigs (oblong moulds). Making pig iron is the first step in the production of ferrous metals. The pig is remelted and the metal run into moulds to form cast iron.

CAST IRON

There are two types of cast iron, grey and white. They get their names from their appearance when fractured, and this will help you to identify any oddment you intend to use. Cast iron is a form of iron that has been melted and poured into a mould, where it has been left until it solidifies. The mould, usually formed from special moulding sand, is made by ramming the sand around a pattern of the object to be moulded.

This process is a cost-effective way of making shaped parts, and is explained in Chapter 7. Cast iron is an alloy of iron and carbon, which may contain small amounts of silicon, manganese, phosphorus and sulphur. An average carbon content is likely to be around 4%.

The carbon present in the white is in the form of cementite, which is intensely hard. This makes the white cast iron very hard and durable, but it is very brittle.

Most of the carbon in the grey is formed by flakes of graphite (the remaining carbon is usually perlite). Grey cast iron is easily worked (the graphite is a lubricant) and is far less brittle than the white. All cast iron has a low tensile strength and poor shock resistance. The grey will be more often encountered than the white, and is more suitable for most of our purposes.

STEEL

PLAIN CARBON STEELS The main difference between cast iron and steel is that while cast iron has around 4% carbon content, plain steel has less than 1.5%. By varying the amount of carbon content, from as low as 0.15% to 1.5%, the characteristics of the metal can be completely changed.

MILD STEEL, containing from 0.15% to 0.3% carbon combined with the iron, is malleable and ductile. It can be brazed and welded, easily machined or worked by hand, and shapes well when forged. It may be worked hot or cold. Because of its low carbon content, it is incapable of being heat-treated to harden it, apart from case hardening.

MEDIUM CARBON STEEL has a carbon content of 0.35% to 0.5%, and is much stronger than mild steel. It can be heat-treated to increase its strength and hardness, and tempered to make it tougher.

HIGH CARBON STEEL has a carbon content of 0.55% to 1.5%. This is the first of the steels mentioned so far that would be suitable for making tools capable of being sharpened and retaining a cutting edge (*see* Fig 2.2). Most of the old chisels and plane irons that take a very sharp edge are made

Fig 2.2 *Old car springs are a good source of high carbon steel.*

from this material, and are usually stamped 'cast steel'.

ALLOY STEELS In recent times, various substances other than carbon have been added to iron to make it more suitable for special applications. Some of these substances are already present in very small quantities with other impurities and trace elements.

■ *Manganese* is added to improve the steel's mechanical properties. Wear on bulldozer blades is lessened by using steel with a high manganese content.

■ *Chromium* and *molybdenum* are added to increase hardness, but not brittleness. Chromium also improves the corrosion resistance of the steel, while molybdenum reduces temper brittleness and allows an alloy to operate continuously at high temperatures without becoming brittle.

■ *Vanadium* improves the elasticity.

■ *Tungsten*, a very hard element, improves the grain structure of the steel to which it is added. It also confers the property of 'red hardness', i.e. the ability to hold an edge even at red heat. Other minerals are added to steels made for special use, such as magnets and heat-resistant surfaces.

STAINLESS STEEL is principally made by alloying iron with nickel and chromium. It is made, as its name implies, to resist corrosion. There are several different forms of this metal. Because the basic alloy can be very difficult to manipulate, an agent is sometimes added to improve its working qualities.

SILVER STEEL This is a tool steel with a carbon content of 1.1% to 1.2%, also containing 0.35% manganese, 0.45% chromium and varying amounts of silicon, 0.2% being typical. This is a very useful material for our purpose. The major tool shops stock it in round bars 13in long. It can be forged with some difficulty, and heat-treated to make woodcutting tools.

HIGH-SPEED STEELS These steels are used for metal cutting tools. They are high carbon steels with heavy additions of tungsten and other rare metals; these additions are made to prevent the hardness from being drawn by the great heat that is developed during cutting. These steels cannot be worked without special facilities. Large machine hacksaw blades that have been scrapped can be ground to make flat cutting tools.

STELLITE AND TUNGSTEN CARBIDE These materials will maintain their hardness even up to a dull red heat. They are not steels and cannot be softened by any heat treatment, which is a disadvantage, and we are unable to use them except where they can be brazed on to a cutting edge.

NONFERROUS METALS

ALUMINIUM

Aluminium is too soft to use in its pure state, and is usually alloyed with magnesium, manganese and copper. When alloyed it is often called 'Duralumin', which is really a trade name applied to an alloy of 97% aluminium with copper, manganese, magnesium and silicon. Aluminium alloy is easily worked and a good conductor of electricity, but is impossible to solder by the usual method.

COPPER

Copper is a ductile, soft material, with a low tensile strength, which solders and brazes with ease. For our purposes, copper is more often used as a base for brass and bronze alloys. It work-hardens but is easily annealed by being heated to a dull red and then being allowed to cool.

TIN

Tin in its pure form will not be met with. For most applications it is alloyed with other metals and used in soft solder, where it is alloyed with lead.

BRASS

Brass is an alloy of copper and zinc. The proportions of alloy can vary, but there must be at least 50% of copper for the alloy to be called brass.

Because of this wide range of proportions, the alloy's characteristics can be changed – as more copper is included the material becomes more ductile. The colour of the alloy is some indication of the amount of copper it contains: a brass with 90% copper will be more red than one with only 60%.

Brass is an ideal material for many small tools. It is very easy to work by hand, and can be easily soldered with both hard and soft solder. English standard brass is 66.6% copper, 33.3% zinc.

Other metals are sometimes added to the brass alloy to impart certain characteristics: tin in quantities of around 2% is added to make the alloy harder, and also improves resistance to corrosion; aluminium greatly increases the strength and hardness; nickel lightens the colour and improves the shear strength, also improving corrosion resistance; manganese is added to high tensile brasses and acts as a deoxidant. Sometimes brass to which manganese has been added is known as 'manganese bronze'.

BRONZE

The term bronze is applied to alloys with a copper and tin base. The alloy is modified for different uses by adding various elements, the main ones being aluminium, manganese and silicon.

GUN METAL The Admiralty specification for gun metal is: copper 88%, tin 10%, zinc 2%. The high content of tin makes the alloy harder than brass, and it is an ideal metal for casting small planes and their like. With age it takes on a very fine patina.

ALUMINIUM BRONZE is composed of 90% copper, 10% aluminium. It casts very well, and is highly suitable for plane bodies. This alloy has high strength and good working properties coupled with resistance to corrosion.

PHOSPHOR BRONZE has 90% copper, 9.5% tin, 0.5% phosphorus. This metal makes fine clean castings.

TELLING ONE TYPE OF METAL FROM ANOTHER

There are of course many more metals, some of which you may find useful. If you have a piece you are thinking of using and are uncertain as to exactly what it is, a few experiments will help you to decide if it is suitable. Inspection should indicate if it is ferrous or nonferrous; hardness can be tested with a file – if it is hard it can probably be annealed (*see* Chapter 6) – and the colour should give some indication as to its make-up if it is a brass alloy.

One type of steel can look very much like another, and time can be wasted by making an article from the wrong variety – for instance, a blade that is to be sharpened must come from steel that can be hardened and tempered. With some experience, a fair guide to the make-up of a steel can be determined by observing the sparks made when grinding it. The higher the content of carbon in the steel, the lighter the colour of the sparks.

High carbon steel produces what I can best describe as a secondary bunch of sparks, which burst out from the first bunch. Cast iron will give off a stream of red sparks that burst into a yellow cluster. If you have some steel that you know the composition of, it may be a good idea to experiment. You will then know what to expect when trying to classify an odd piece.

METHODS OF DISTINGUISHING DIFFERENT FERROUS METALS			
Metal on test	**Drop on anvil**	**Nick and hammer in vice**	**Grind on emery wheel**
Cast iron Grey	Dull note	Snaps easily. Coarse dark fracture.	Dark bushy stream with bright bursts.
Cast iron White	Very dull note	Clean break. Fine white fracture.	Dark red stream close to wheel.
Wrought iron	Dull metallic note	Bends well. Fibrous structure clearly seen.	Fine stream of bright sparks.
Mild steel	Medium pitched ring	Bends before breaking. Shows uniform grey lustre on fracture.	Long white sparks in extended stream with primary bursts.
Cast steel	High ringing note	Bends a little then breaks off. Silvery, fine crystalline fracture.	Secondary white bursts from bushy bright stream.
High-speed steel	Medium metallic ring	Resists blow and then breaks clean. Very fine crystalline fracture.	Dull red sparks close to wheel.

TIMBER

I am sure the reader will feel more at home with this material than the metals previously described. The saying, 'Men who work metal become hard and cold as steel, unlike the people that work wood, who are kind and warm like their materials', is grossly unfair: the help and advice freely given by engineers has enabled me to make most of the tools described in this book.

I still prefer to work wood, finding metal an unkind material. Timber in some form plays a part in nearly all the tools that we wish to make. Sometimes it is not present in the finished item, but was used to construct a pattern to make the mould into which the metal was cast. There are many different timbers that will fulfil most purposes for making tools. A general discussion of what is needed of a timber for each use in toolmaking follows, but the reader should remember that no two pieces of the same species of timber are the same. It therefore follows that, while one piece might well be suitable, another from the same species might have to be rejected.

WOOD FOR PATTERN MAKING

Two features should be present in timber if it is to make a good pattern: first, it should be mild-grained, so it can be freely worked. Wood with this feature is also stable, and this is most important. Second, it must glue well, as many patterns are just shaped blocks butt-glued together.

Certain woods have been favourites with pattern makers since patterns have been made. Canadian yellow pine (*Pinus strobus* (S)) is one of these, but it has become very expensive in recent years, and jelutong (*Dyera costulata*) from Malaya is used extensively nowadays.

Provided that a mild straight-grained piece is selected, Honduras mahogany (*Swietenia*

macrophylla) can be used. In the trade this timber is only used when there are several castings to be made from the same pattern, as it is harder than the two woods mentioned above, and stands up to hard treatment.

WOODEN PLANE BODIES

Beech (*Fagus sylvatica*) has long been the first choice of plane makers in this country. That does not mean that it is the only suitable wood, or the best one – many craftsmen have fashioned some beautiful tools from exotic hardwoods.

On the continent, hornbeam (*Carpinus betulus* (H)) is often used; Ulmia, a German manufacturer, produces a very fine smoother with a pearwood (*Pyrus communis* (H)) body and a lignum vitae (*Guaiacum officinale*) sole. The main requirements are for a stable wood that will wear evenly.

INFILL FOR METAL PLANES

Rosewood (*Dalbergia nigra*) has traditionally been used as an infill and for the handles. As we are talking about the Rolls-Royces of planes, it is only fitting that only the very finest wood is used. On some of the small bronze planes described in later chapters, blackwood (*Dalbergia melanoxylon*) is used, as its black colour looks good against the bronze.

CHISEL AND SCREWDRIVER HANDLES

Boxwood (*Buxus sempervirens*) has always been used on the best tools, but unfortunately has become difficult to obtain in recent years. I have been using lemonwood (*Calycophyllum candidissimum*) as a replacement for boxwood, with pleasing results. It will be seen from the foregoing that the choice of wood is mainly common sense: a splintery wood is obviously unsuitable for a handle, and whether or not the handle is on a tool that will require driving with a mallet also has a bearing on which wood is suitable.

GLUE

There are two situations where glue will be needed. The first is where wood needs to be glued to wood, as in making up an infill, for instance. Most woodworkers will have the type they normally use in their workshop readily available. Many of the more exotic woods do not glue very well, because they are oily, and these should be degreased before applying the glue.

Most of the tools are reproductions of items that were made when only hot-melt animal-based glues were available – these glues have proved their worth by keeping tools together up to the present, so I stick to tradition and use them. The best alternative is to use aliphatic resin glue (Franklin Titebond), which I can recommend: it has a much better grab than PVA (see below) and is not fugitive. It sets fairly quickly, so cramps and holding devices are not held up for long.

There are occasions when it is desirable to glue wood to metal, and this is best done by using Araldite or another similar epoxy resin glue. The wood and metal both need degreasing before the joint is made. The standard Araldite is best: the ten-minute short-cure version is not as strong, so, unless the time factor is important, do not use it.

For pattern making there is nothing to beat ordinary PVA. It is clean-working and needs no preparation; this is ideal, as glue is constantly required in small quantities. Many joints in a pattern can be held with panel pins while the glue sets.

FINISHES

Apart from the need to protect some surfaces against corrosion, finish is a matter of taste.

Most woods require some form of treatment, even if it is only a rub over with a linseed-oiled rag. Rosewood looks its best when French polished: a good quality button polish brings out the beauty of the wood and is fairly hard-wearing. Beech tools are usually soaked in linseed oil until the grain is full; this adds to the weight and protects against moisture. I have seen some tools finished with modern two-pack resin varnish, but to my mind this gives them a cheap plastic look if it is overdone.

METAL FINISHES

When it comes to finishing metal, there is a decision to be made – is it to be undertaken by the maker or is it to be sent to a specialist metal finisher? It is beyond the scope of wood workshops to electroplate on metal, and that means that for most of us, apart from buffing and polishing or enamelling, the item will be sent away and we will get a bill. Even so, if a lot of time and effort has gone into making a tool, the finish can make or mar the final appearance.

POLISHING AND BUFFING

When the construction of a tool is finished, a multitude of small marks will be left on the surface of the metal. These scratches and grinding marks not only spoil the appearance of the tool, but are places in which corrosive substances can be retained.

When working, perspiration from the hands is transferred to the metal surfaces of the tool and is a main cause of corrosion. A highly polished surface is easy to wipe clean and to keep lubricated with a thin film of oil.

A mirror-like finish can be obtained by using wet and dry abrasive paper. The grade of paper used to start with depends on the depth of the surface marks, and care should be taken not to start with too coarse a grade, which will only add to the scratches; 280 is about the limit.

For flat finishes the paper is best stuck down on a flat surface – double-sided adhesive is best for this purpose. The tool is rubbed on the paper, using kerosene as a lubricant. When on inspection the only scratches that show are those made by the abrasive paper, the wet and dry is replaced with a sheet of a finer grade.

This procedure continues until a good surface is reached using 1200 grade. The final paper used is crocus polishing paper. The area should be kept clear of any grit that may contaminate the paper surface and scratch the work.

Buffing is a machine process, and does not replace the hand work described above. The only part that it can do is that of final polishing – all scratches and surface marks must be removed first.

The buffing machine is best described as a power-driven spindle with a tapered thread at each end. (In the trade this thread is called the pig's tail.) The thread is right-handed on the right-hand end and left-handed on the left-hand end. As the spindle revolves towards the operator, the buffing mop tightens on the spindle as it turns.

Buffing compound, supplied in stick form, is applied to the revolving mop. The workpiece is pushed against the mop and moved about so that the mop moves over the whole surface to be buffed. As the item being buffed can become quite hot, there is a temptation to hold it with a piece of rag. This is a very dangerous procedure to adopt, as the rag can very easily become drawn on to the spindle, taking the operator's hand with it. For the occasional job, a short spindle with a pig's tail at one end can be obtained to fit into the chuck of an electric drill.

Buffing compound comes in several grades; a separate mop should be kept for each grade. Mops are usually made of calico, and small felt ones are obtainable for internal surfaces. After buffing, carry on to complete the polishing with a clean rag and a little metal polish.

GUN BLACK

Gunsmiths and shops dealing in firearms sell proprietary products to turn the surface of steel a dull black. This finish is highly suitable for the blades of try squares and similar tools. However, it tends to wear through very easily and it is sometimes a good policy to protect it with a coat of lacquer. There are several different makes of gun black, and each comes complete with instructions.

LACQUERING

Applying a coat of lacquer or varnish to a metallic surface that has been previously coloured or polished will protect its surface. The application may be made by brushing, dipping or spraying. It may be applied to a cold or hot surface – a hot surface will make the material flow out more evenly and promotes quick drying. Spraying gives the best results, and is to be recommended for those workshops that have the correct equipment.

The metal is first cleaned of grease, and is then warmed in an oven. When it has been coated, if the facilities exist, it should be returned to the oven, which has been turned off. This allows the item to cool down slowly and protects the tacky surface from dust.

The lacquer used should be one that is made for metal, as others have a tendency to peel off. Bright brass items that are not handled a lot, such as lever caps on planes, look well finished this way. Some craftsmen prefer the oxidized surface of nonferrous metal, and lacquer can be applied to this with good effect.

Sometimes metals are dipped in an acid mixture and washed under hot running water before lacquering. This procedure provides a surface that is spotlessly clean and one to which the lacquer will adhere better than one that is untreated. Brass can be dipped in a solution of 10 parts sulphuric acid, 5 parts nitric acid and 5 parts water. Be careful, as this is a highly corrosive mix – wear rubber gloves and eye protection, and **always add the acid to the water**, not the water to the acid.

PAINTING AND ENAMELLING

There is nothing that can spoil the look of a good tool more than a coat of poorly applied paint. The technique looks so easy that any fool should be able to do it with ease, but it is important that the materials used are of the best quality obtainable; this same rule applies to the brushes.

The amount of paint required to cover the average painted parts of a tool could easily be contained in an eggcup, so only a small tin is required, and it is a false economy to try and make do. That paint left over from a previous job may look alright once the skin has been removed, but is it?

Brushes must be looked after; those that have been standing in a tin of turps since they were last used are in no way suitable. The brushes sold in most DIY shops are of poor quality – a good ½in brush will cost several pounds, but looked after properly will last for years. However, if spraying facilities are available, they are to be preferred to brush application.

The type and make of paint used as a finish will determine what base coats are needed. The best approach is to buy the finish first and then read the manufacturers' instructions, which invariably give details of which base coats will be required for the paint. The application procedure is the same as described above for lacquer. Hammer and crackle finishes are also possible, but should not be used indiscriminately, as they do not look well on tools of an older design.

STOVE ENAMELLING

Stove enamel should not be confused with vitreous enamel. Stove enamelling is a method of applying a paint that is specially formulated to dry rapidly at a high temperature in an oven. Vitreous enamelling is a method of fusing molten coloured glass on to steel or aluminium alloy sheet.

Stove enamelling is a technique requiring special apparatus not to be found in the woodwork shop. There are firms specializing in this process, and the finish they can put on to a steel casting is well worth the price.

ELECTROPLATING

Electrodeposition is a means by which one metal can be surface coated with a thin layer of another metal. When an electric current is passed through a solution of metallic salts, the solution is decomposed and the pure metal is chemically precipitated.

Metals commonly deposited in this way are copper, nickel, chrome, cadmium and silver. While it is possible to set up a small plating bath using a car battery, the results obtained do not warrant the effort involved – it is by far the best policy to take the work to a local metal finisher. A useful feature of electroplating is that the finisher can remove old defective plating by reversing the process and then replating.

NICKEL PLATING

Nickel plate can be either bright or dull. Bright nickel is probably the most attractive and durable finish on cast steel tools. When it comes to refurbishing some of the early tools, this finish makes them look better than new.

Items to be nickel plated should first be plated with copper, which gives a better and more durable finish, and all surfaces to be plated should be smooth and free from scratches and grinding marks, as any blemish in the surface will show on the finished item. On some items that are cast and that would be difficult to polish, for instance an old Stanley 45 plane, dull nickel looks better than bright. Most of the early tools by Preston and similar manufacturers were nickel plated.

CHROMIUM PLATE

This has never been a popular finish with toolmakers, probably because it is somewhat more expensive than nickel and can look quite garish. For a really good job it needs plating on top of copper and nickel. The only job that I have had chrome plated peeled after a short while. The edges of the chrome were razor sharp and the job was a disaster, so I am loath to recommend it. I have a honing guide that has been black chromed on aluminium alloy – this is a very elegant finish and is lasting well.

ANODIZING

Anodic oxidation, or anodizing, is an electrolytic process for thickening the oxide film present on aluminium surfaces. This oxide film may be dyed to any desired colour. Like other metal finishes, anodizing does not cover up marks and scratches, but greatly emphasises them.

Tools Required to Make Tools

THREE GROUPS

The tools required to construct fine woodworking tools fall into three groups. These are: bench metalworking tools, precision measuring and marking tools, and basic woodworking tools. This last group will not need describing in any detail, as anyone interested enough to wish to make fine woodworking tools will already be more than familiar with what is required.

The manufacture of certain items will need some metal turning, and a lathe must be used. Depending on the ingenuity of the individual, a lot can be done by adapting a wood lathe or pillar drill. (Engineering craftsmen will no doubt think this a load of old rubbish!)

Apart from the adjusters on my planes, all parts have been made without any metalcutting machinery. There is no point in an individual who wishes to own fine woodworking tools rushing out and purchasing a lot of metalworking tools. The money so spent might just as well have been invested in the woodworking tools to start with, thus saving a lot of time. The metalworking tools described are therefore divided between those that are essential and those that are helpful.

Because of the recent change to metric measurement in this country, engineering firms have had to change all their measuring equipment. A lot of imperial equipment no longer required by industry has come on to the secondhand market, with very few purchasers interested in it. This has been a once in a lifetime chance for the amateur to own tools that could otherwise never have been purchased.

THE HACKSAW

The hacksaw will be one of the most used tools – in many woodwork shops one already

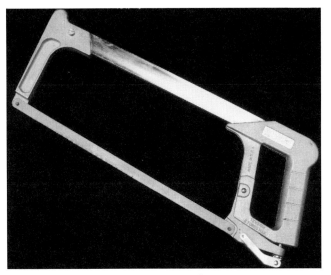

Fig 3.1 Ideal pattern of adjustable hacksaw frame.

Fig 3.2 Junior hacksaw frames. The lower one is to be preferred.

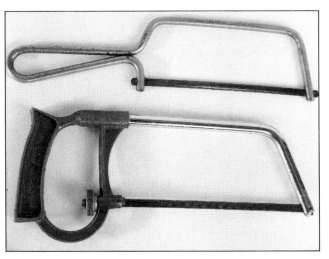

exists, but is often neglected, with the blade misused and employed on all gauges of metal.

The frame should be adjustable, so that blades of various lengths can be used. Provision should also be made for inserting the blade at right angles to the frame, which will enable long cuts to be made without the frame fouling the metal (*see* Fig 3.1).

Most woodworkers prefer a pistol grip-handled frame to the file handle type used by most fitters. A junior hacksaw will also be required, and an adjustable tension variety is to be preferred. The type where the frame is just a bent-up steel rod allows the blade to flex, making it impossible to make an accurate cut (*see* Fig 3.2).

The blades used should be matched to the work that is to be cut. Blades are available with the number of teeth per inch from 14 to 32; this is known as the pitch.

Three different pitched blades need to be held in stock: 14, 18 and 24. The length of the blade best suited to this class of work is 12in, although the longest blade possible will be a help if a large casting has to be cut.

Junior hacksaw blades come in one pitch and length. Blades are also classified by their flexibility. High-speed steel blades, sometimes known as 'all hard', perform best on all types of metal, but unfortunately they are very brittle and easily broken.

A more forgiving variety consists of a bimetal blade, which has a cutting edge of high-speed steel welded to a more flexible back. There is also the flexible blade – this will stand a good deal of mistreatment, but wears out much faster than the two previously mentioned types. A blade with graduated teeth is also available, but is not a lot of use for our sort of work.

The hacksaw blade's teeth are set similar to those on a woodcutting saw. The blade cuts a kerf wider than the gauge of the blade; as the saw wears the set is reduced, and for that reason a new blade must not be run in the kerf that an old one has cut.

FILES

Files are classified by three different features: length, cross-section and cut. The length of a file is stated in inches, and is the distance from the shoulder below the tang to the end of the blade. There are several different cross-sections, the principal ones being: square, flat, half round, round and knife edge (*see* Figs 3.3(a), 3.3(b) and 3.3(c)).

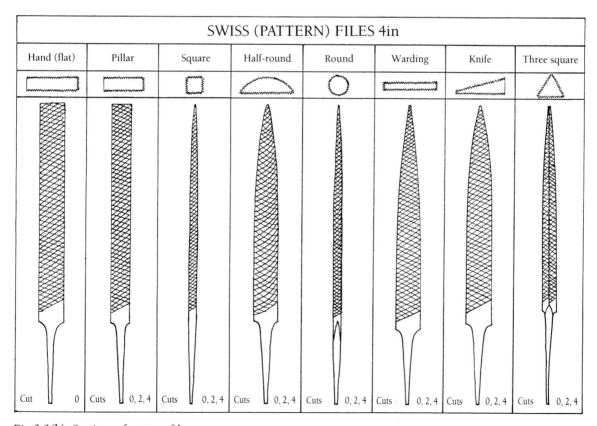

Fig 3.3(a) Sections of general engineering files.

Fig 3.3(b) Sections of pattern files.

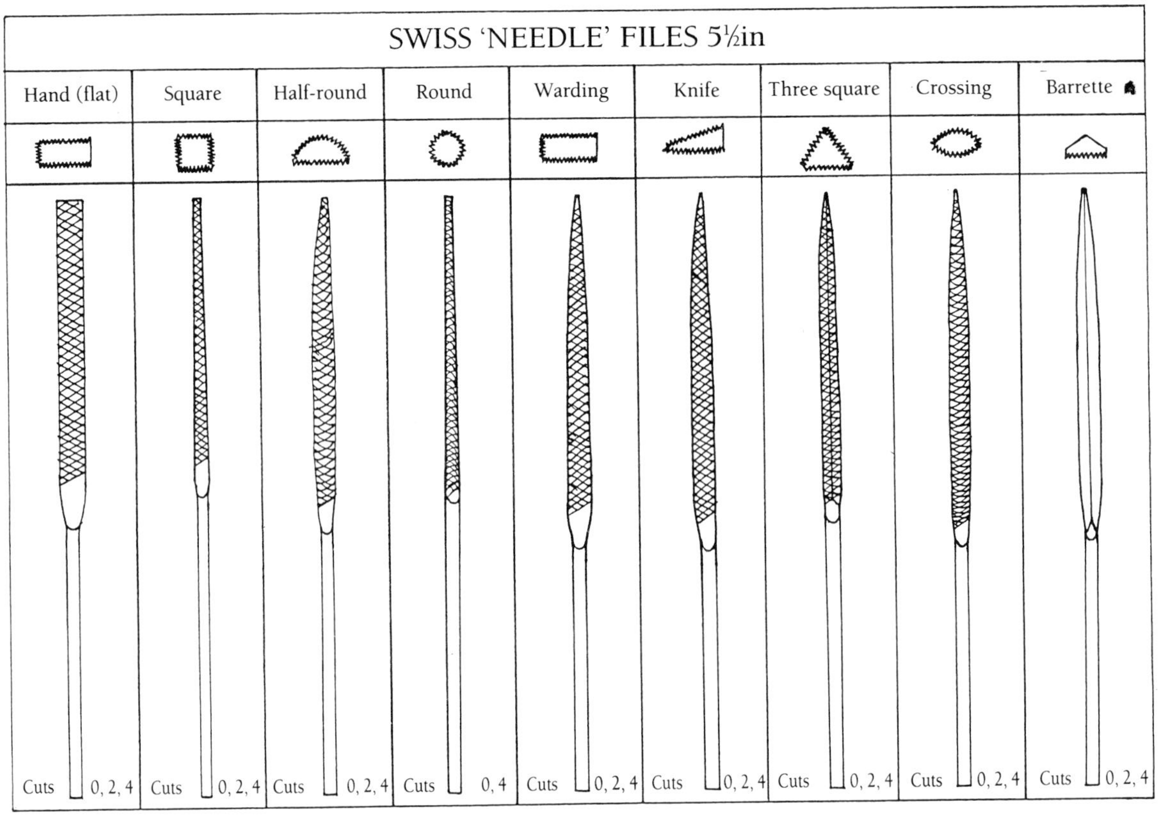

SWISS 'NEEDLE' FILES 5½in								
Hand (flat)	Square	Half-round	Round	Warding	Knife	Three square	Crossing	Barrette ♠
Cuts 0, 2, 4	Cuts 0, 2, 4	Cuts 0, 2, 4	Cuts 0, 4	Cuts 0, 2, 4	Cuts 0, 2, 4	Cuts 0, 2, 4	Cuts 0, 2, 4	Cuts 0, 2, 4

Fig 3.3(c) Sections of needle files (5½in).

The cut is the pattern of the teeth, and it may be single or double. A single cut has the teeth parallel to one another and at an angle to the centre line of the file. The double cut has a second cut made over and at an angle to the first. This produces pyramid-shaped teeth with more cutting edges, and is the most used cut (*see* Fig 3.4).

The size of the teeth are graded and named as follows (coarsest first): rough, bastard, second cut, smooth and dead smooth (*see* Fig 3.5). There is also a special cut known as the dreadnought, which is used for the very rapid removal of metal.

The files that will be required most often are: the bastard, which is used for the fast removal of metal, but leaves a rough surface; the second cut, for the more precise shaping; and a smooth cut file for the final finishing.

The size of the file is reflected in the size of the teeth. For example, a 10in smooth file will have larger teeth than a 6in smooth file. All files should be fitted with handles. Not only is the file easier to use with one fitted, it is also a safety precaution as the point at the end of the tang can be very sharp, and can easily stick into the palm of the user's hand. When purchased, files do not have handles fitted, so the handle can, and should, be the first tool that you make.

The files mentioned so far are the main ones that will be used for most metal shaping jobs. When it comes to more delicate fitting work, needle files will be required. These are

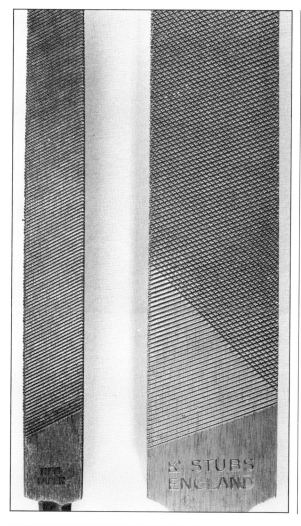

small files used on very fine and delicate work. They do not have a sharp tang like other files; their tang is shaped into a cylindrical handle. The pitch of the teeth varies from 40 to 200 teeth per inch (*see* Fig 3.6).

There are 13 different shapes of needle file. These are not all needed, but those in bold type will be found most useful. They are: oval, pippin, knife, barrette, slitting, **round edge joint**, hand, **warding**, **three square**, square, half-round, round and crossing.

Several other types of file may be met with – for instance, the tapered saw file, which is found in abundance in the woodwork shop, can be very useful.

FILES MOST OFTEN USED

The blade of the **flat file** is tapered in width and thickness. It is usually double cut on both

Fig 3.4 Single and double cut file teeth.

Fig 3.5 (below left) Different grades of teeth on flat files. Left to right: coarse, bastard, second cut, smooth.

Fig 3.6 (below right) Needle files – the handle can be fitted to any one of the files, and is less tiring on the fingers

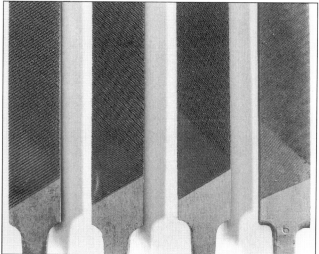

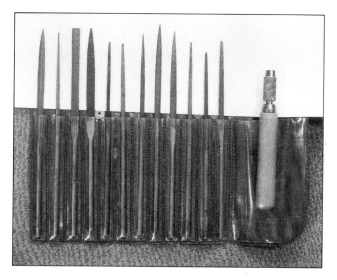

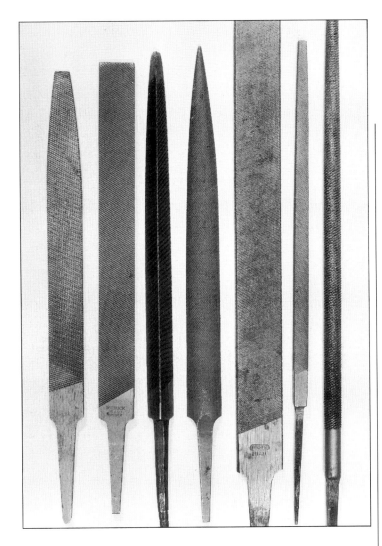

Fig 3.7 Selection of files. Left to right: hand, flat, three square, half round, square, round.

The **round file** is also known as the **rat-tail**. This is used for enlarging holes and cleaning up shaped cut-outs. One about ¼in in diameter will be needed.

The **half-round file** is not half of a circle, as its name would have us believe. In section it is only a segment of a circle. The first third of the blade's length is tapered and the flat face is usually single cut.

The **riffler** can best be described as a bent file. It comes in a variety of shapes and is used for cleaning up awkward internal shapes. Rifflers can be useful, but are seldom needed.

THE CARE OF FILES

The file is a fundamental metalworking tool and needs some care if it is to stay in good working condition. Major damage is caused to the teeth if files are stored loose in a drawer. They knock against one another and, being hard and brittle, the teeth are easily chipped. The best method of parking them is to hang them up when they are not being used.

In use the file's teeth tend to become clogged up with the metal they are removing. A **file card**, best described as a short-haired wire brush, should be frequently used to clear the teeth of this metal (*see* Fig 3.8). Soft metals such as aluminium are particularly prone to causing this problem. It helps if a stick of chalk is rubbed along the teeth of the file before using it. When the metal stuck in the teeth of the file cannot be removed with the file card, each individual tooth gullet must be cleaned with a pin. Failure to keep the file clean will result in deep scratches on the workpiece.

faces and single cut on its edges, and is a very useful general-purpose tool (*see* Fig 3.7).

The **hand file** is parallel both in thickness and in width. The faces are most often double cut – while one edge is single cut, the other lacks teeth and is left smooth. This edge is termed a 'safe edge': it allows cuts to be made right up into internal corners without damage to the surface that the safe edge rubs against.

Triangular files are known to engineers as **three square**. I find that saw files are ideal for the same purposes as a triangular file. The double-ended variety is particularly useful when cleaning up dovetails in metal.

Square files have the first third of their length tapered; the teeth are double cut on all faces. While it can be a useful tool, the purchase of one can well be left until the need arises.

Fig 3.8 (top) Cleaning file teeth. From top to bottom: clogged file, small file card, length of file card.

Fig 3.9 (middle) Scrapers. From top to bottom; flat, half round, triangular.

Fig 3.10 (bottom) The scrapers in Fig 3.9 rotated through 90°.

SCRAPERS

Engineer's scrapers come in three shapes: flat, half-round and three-corner (*see* Figs 3.9 and 3.10). The scraper is a very useful tool, particularly when trueing flat surfaces, and the good news is that there is no need to buy one – because of the high quality steel files are made from, old worn-out files can be made into very fine scrapers.

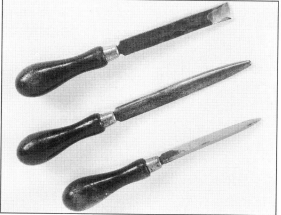

The old file will need softening, forging to shape, filing and then rehardening. The technique used to do this is described in Chapter 6. It is also possible to make a scraper by grinding all the teeth off an old file, great care being taken not to draw the temper by getting the metal hot. This might sound easier than all that heat treatment, but either way you have another tool that you have manufactured for yourself.

COLD CHISELS

Just mentioning the name cold chisel conjures up in some people's minds that much-abused tool used to cut holes in brick walls. The chisels that will be needed are far removed from that image. Because most woodworkers who make their own tools will not have access to metal cutting machinery, the cold chisel is a very important tool. The term 'cold' refers to the fact that the tool is used to shape metal in its cold state, as opposed to that which is worked hot, as in forging. The cold chisel is manufactured in four shapes: flat, cross-cut, half-round and diamond point.

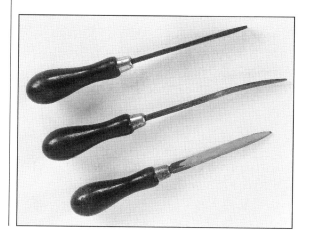

The **flat chisel** is the most common type and is the variety that will be used most. It can be used for cutting off and for surfacing. The cross-cut is used for roughing out and grooving. We will not have much use for the diamond point or the half-round in our sort of work.

Several flat chisels of varying size will be needed. Purchase one about ¾in wide at the cutting edge to start with. When it has been used for a time, you can determine what other sizes are required. If you buy a cross-cut, a cutting edge ³⁄₁₆in wide is a good size. Once the technique of heat-treating steel has been mastered, any chisel can be made in the workshop, so it is wise only to purchase what is essential to start with.

PUNCHES

A **centre punch** will be required, as this is an essential tool. It is made of high carbon steel, hardened and tempered in a similar way to a cold chisel. The point of the punch is ground to a conical shape.

The main purpose for which the punch will be used is to mark the centre of holes that are to be drilled. This not only indicates the position, but also stops the drill point from wandering when the hole is being started. It is also used for other marking out jobs, like the centre of a circle. The indentation made by the punch stops the dividers' legs from slipping all over the place.

The **dot or prick punch** is a similar tool to a centre punch, the difference being the point is much finer, being ground at a less acute angle. This tool is used when setting out, to mark the position of scribed lines that may become obliterated. This use is dealt with in Chapter 5.

The **automatic centre punch**, whilst not an essential tool, can save quite a bit of time (*see* Fig 3.11). There is an internal spring mechanism inside the tool, and when the point is placed in position on the work, pressure is applied to the tool. The mechanism releases energy from the spring, and the point is driven into the workpiece. The amount of energy that the spring can store is adjustable, enabling shallow or deep marks to be made. There are often quite a number of marks required when setting out, and while these are normally made with the dot punch, the automatic punch is much quicker.

TWIST DRILLS

While there are other types of metal cutting drill, the only sort freely available and suitable for our purpose is the twist drill. This tool

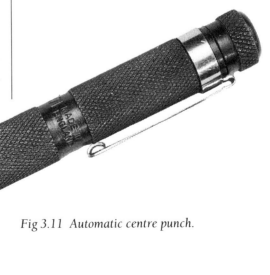

Fig 3.11 Automatic centre punch.

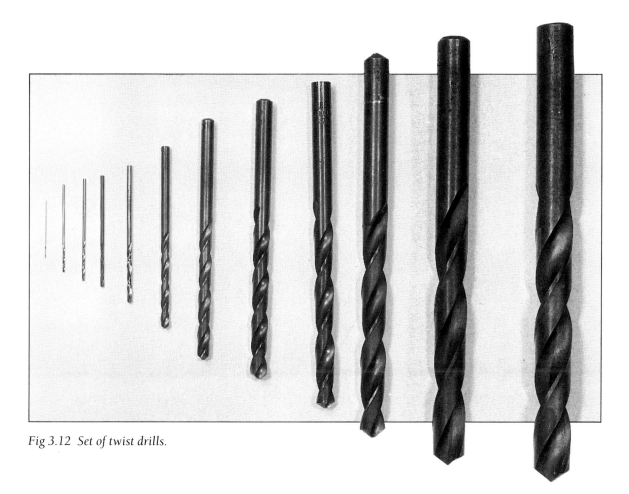

Fig 3.12 Set of twist drills.

may look quite simple, but close examination reveals various angles to the cutting edge and clearances on the flute, which make it quite complex (see Fig 3.12).

There will be a lot of drilling, as this is a most effective way of cutting out shaped parts from flat plate. If the workshop has a pillar or bench drill, a lot of time will be saved, but it is not an essential item. Most pillar drills are fitted with a quill that has a Morse taper – this is a much better way of holding a large diameter drill than in a chuck.

The workshop should be equipped with a fairly comprehensive set of drills: maybe six about ⅛in in diameter should always be to hand. These are for cutting out, and their exact diameter is not important. Drills larger than ½in need only be obtained when needed for a specific purpose.

TAPS AND DIES

From time to time there will be a need to cut threads, both internal and external.
Fortunately, there are few threaded parts on woodworking tools, and the acquisition of this equipment can be left until it is necessary; then only what is required for the job in hand need be purchased. Whitworth taps and dies are frequently to be found secondhand: this is an obsolete thread in industry, and Whitworth is an ideal thread for the woodworker, as in its larger sizes it works well on wood. This equipment can replace a tap and screw box for cutting wooden threads, as even a secondhand screw box is an expensive commodity.

A **tap** may be regarded as a bolt with a perfect thread cut on it that has been provided with cutting edges (see Fig 3.13). When it is screwed into a hole it cuts an internal thread.

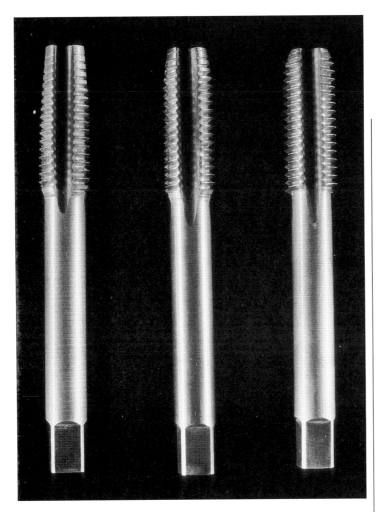

Fig 3.13 *Set of taps – note how the tips are ground. Left to right: taper, intermediate, plug.*

The **die** consists of a nut that has had a portion of its thread circumference cut away to form a cutting edge. There are several different types of die, but for our purposes only the split die will be considered. To manipulate the die it must be placed into a holder called a die stock. The die cuts a male thread on tubes or round bar. When purchasing stocks and dies, it is important to make sure that the stocks fit the outer diameter of the die.

REAMERS

The reamer is a tool that will seldom be required, but you should be aware of it. On the odd occasion when a hole of exact size is required, this is the only hand tool that can produce it. The reamer consists of a rod of tool steel, fluted to present a series of cutting edges along its length. There should be an odd number of these cutting edges, as this prevents the tendency to produce an eccentric hole. The flutes are sometimes ground spirally to give a sweeter cut (*see* Fig 3.14). A variety of adjustable reamer is manufactured, and can be useful when making an exact hole to fit a ground bar.

THE BROACH

The broach (Lancashire pattern) is a tool for enlarging the size of a hole; there are other patterns, but the Lancashire is the best. It consists of a length of tapered metal with five flat sides. This pentagonal shape gives the tool five cutting corners. At the end of the broach there is a square section on to which a tap wrench can be fitted. The small end of the tool is inserted through the hole to be enlarged, and the broach is fed forward whilst being turned. This action scrapes metal from the

Taps are made from high carbon steel and hardened; they are brittle and can easily be chipped or broken. The shank of the tap is left plain with a square end to fit a tap wrench.

Taps are usually supplied in sets of three to cut one size of thread. These are called taper, intermediate and bottoming; or taper, second and plug. The taper has the first 8 to 10 threads at its end ground to a taper. This enables the end to enter the hole that is to be tapped, and to cut to the full depth of the thread gradually.

The second tap only has two or three threads chamfered away at the end. This tap follows the thread cut by the first, and is suitable for finishing the thread of holes that go right through the metal.

The plug tap is not ground away at the end like the other two. It is used to cut a thread right to the bottom of blind holes.

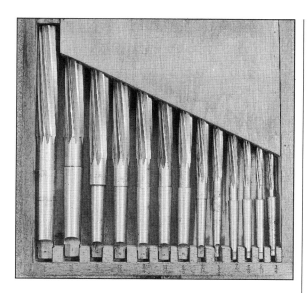

Fig 3.14 *Set of reamers. Note the spiral fluting.*

inside of the hole. The broach is a useful, but not essential tool.

MEASURING AND MARKING TOOLS

Accurate measuring and marking out are fundamental to all the processes that will be used in tool making. I cannot overemphasize how important it is to work accurately – if the tools made are to be superior to those obtainable from retail tool shops, every operation in their manufacture must be to the highest standard. The whole process starts with setting out, and to set out accurately we must be able to measure precisely.

Before even starting to measure, we are confronted with the problem of what system of measurement to use. As previously stated, I am committed to the imperial inch, but this unfortunately does not completely solve the problem of how the inch will be subdivided. Woodworkers use the 'divide by two' method, e.g. half, quarter, eighth and so on. Engineers use the tenth, hundredth and thousandth

system. Because micrometers and verniers are only obtainable in the tenths system, I use a mixture of both. This is not as confusing as it may seem.

RULES

A 6in and 12in rule will cover all our needs. There is one thing that I would strongly counsel – never have a rule that has both tenths and eighths on it. It is so easy to measure ⅝in when what was wanted was 0.6in. The ideal rule has the whole length of one edge divided in the same way (*see* Fig 3.15). Rules with the first inch or so divided in hundredths, then the next in twentieths, etc., etc., are a nuisance. The ideal rule will have an edge in fiftieths, another in twentieths, one in tenths and the last in hundredths. You will need a magnifying glass, but I did say work accurately!

The edge of the rule will occasionally be used as a straightedge, so make sure it is

Fig 3.15 *Steel rule ends showing the ideal markings on each of the edges.*

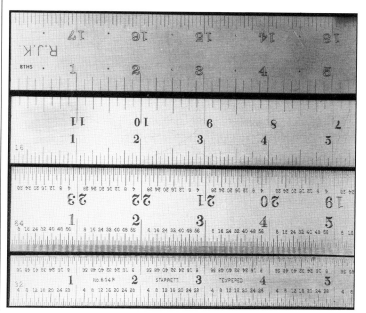

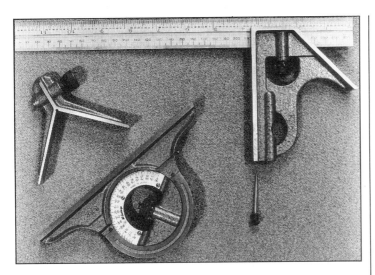

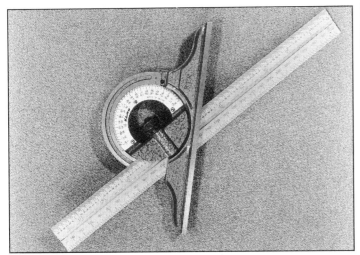

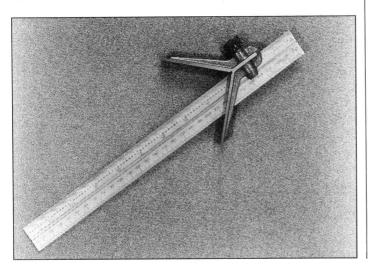

straight before trusting it. Rules are precision instruments and should be treated as such: the end of the rule is not a scraper or a lever for opening tins. When rules are not being used they should be stored in a drawer with other measuring equipment, not left about on the bench top.

COMBINATION SET

The combination set of instruments (sometimes called a combination square) provides most of the basic marking out and measuring tools needed (*see* Fig 3.16). It consists of a protractor head, square head and centre head, and an interchangeable rule, which can be located in any of the heads.

When the rule is placed in the protractor head, a very useful and accurate bevel gauge is produced, with the added advantage that the bevel can be read in degrees (*see* Fig 3.17). When the rule is used with the square head, angles of 90° and 45° can be checked or marked. (This setup also acts as a rule stand when working off a surface, which will be explained later.) While the centre head is more limited for our purposes, it is an accurate means of checking 90° angles, and 45° angles when fitted to the rule (*see* Fig 3.18). The rule is often hardened, which makes it an ideal straightedge.

There is usually a small scriber in the stock of the square, which tends to become lost. If purchasing secondhand, check that the scriber is there: you will not necessarily need

Fig 3.16 (top) Combination set – the scriber fits into the stock.

Fig 3.17 (middle) Combination set rigged as a protractor.

Fig 3.18 (bottom) Combination set rigged as a centre finder.

it, but it can be a good way of getting the price reduced. If a combination square is not obtained, then some separate tools will be needed: a 6in engineers' square (*see* Fig 3.19), an engineers' bevel, a protractor with graduated head (*see* Fig 3.20) and a ground and hardened 12in straightedge. From this you will see that the acquisition of a combination square is almost essential and certainly space-saving.

DIVIDERS AND TRAMMELS

The universal tool for marking out circles and arcs is a pair of dividers, which is also useful for transferring measurements from rule to work. They have two similar legs of hardened steel, with scribing points at their ends. There are two patterns of dividers, described as the firm joint and the spring-adjustable. The spring-adjustable is to be preferred, as this type is far easier to set up accurately. A pair of 6in dividers is ideal for most purposes.

Dividers become less accurate and more difficult to use as the radius of the arc being scribed gets larger. This is due to the increased angle that the leg makes with the work, so the point tends to slip out of the indentation made with the centre punch, while the point scribing the line is at a low angle to the surface being marked, and does not scribe a nice line. Trammels are therefore required to mark all radii over about 6in. The trammels illustrated in Fig 3.21 were made in my workshop; they are used primarily for woodworking tasks, but work well on metal.

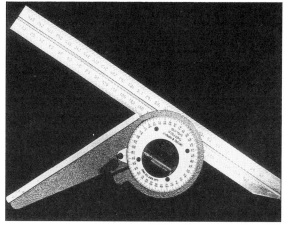

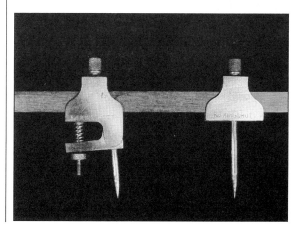

Fig 3.19 (top) Set of engineers' try squares.

Fig 3.20 (middle) Protractor of a different design to that in Fig 3.17.

Fig 3.21 (bottom) Pair of trammels made in my workshop.

INSIDE AND OUTSIDE CALLIPERS

A medium-size (6in) pair of both inside and outside callipers will be found most useful (*see* Fig 3.22). When making parts, the callipers

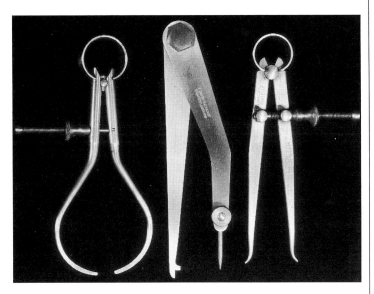

Fig 3.22 Left to right: a pair of outside callipers, odd legs (or hermaphrodites), inside callipers. The pattern with an adjustment screw is to be preferred.

Fig 3.23 Vernier calliper gauges. The top one was bought from a market stall for £2; it has imperial markings on one side and metric on the other. The lower one is new and has imperial and metric markings on the same side.

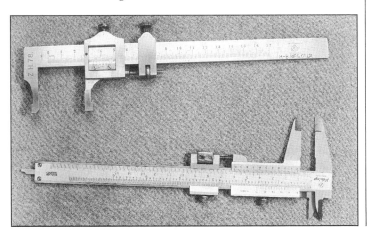

can be used as a gauge by setting them up from a rule to the finished part's dimension. They can also be used to take dimensions from shapes that would be awkward to measure with a rule. As with the dividers, the spring-adjustable pattern is to be preferred.

THE VERNIER CALLIPER GAUGE

The vernier calliper is, I think, an essential item (*see* Fig 3.23). It enables the accurate measuring of inside and outside dimensions, and some models even allow the tool to be used as a depth gauge. To use the callipers, both locking screws are slackened, the jaws are slid open to approximately the size of the item to be measured and the locking screw on the distance bridge is tightened. The jaws are then adjusted to take the measurement with the knurled nut that lies parallel to the scale. The second screw is locked and the gauge removed for reading.

The reading can best be explained by an illustration (*see* Fig 3.24). First, a reading to $\frac{1}{100}$in: the fixed part is marked in tenths, and the slide has ten divisions equal to each other and occupying in all $\frac{9}{10}$in, i.e. each vernier division is 0.09in – one-hundredth less than each of the fixed divisions. When the calliper's jaws are closed, both 0s come in line. Whole numbers, tenths, and then hundredths are read. Thus on Diagram 1 the reading is:

(i)	Whole numbers	0.00
(ii)	Seven complete tenths	0.70
(iii)	Two hundredths (first line on the slide to come opposite a line on the fixed scale)	0.02
	Total	0.72

The actual tool has far smaller divisions than shown above, but works on the same

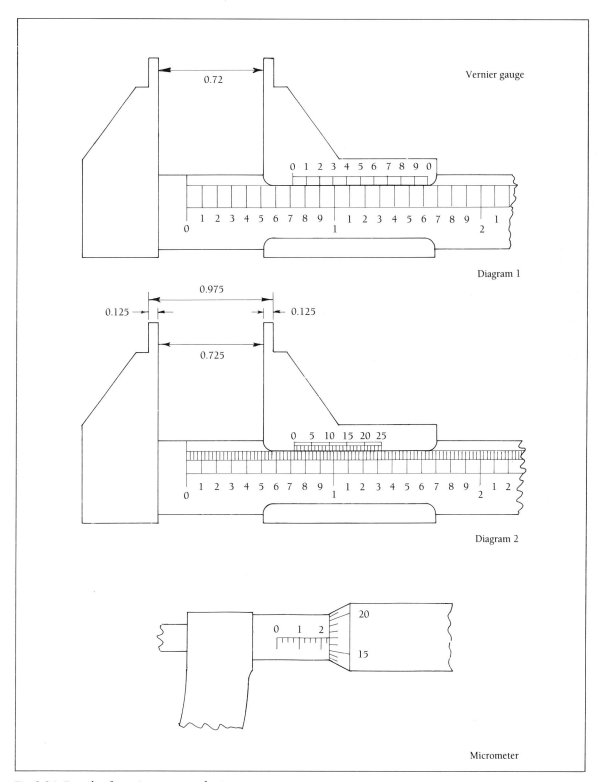

Fig 3.24 *Details of vernier gauge and micrometer.*

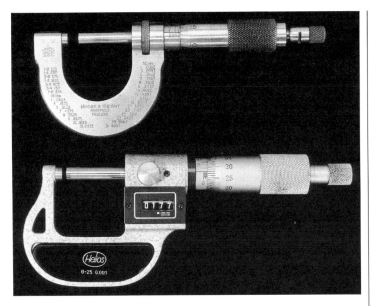

Fig 3.25 Micrometers. The top one is ex-Ministry, made in 1931, with imperial measurements (also bought at a market). The lower one is a modern digital, reading metric.

THE MICROMETER

Although a micrometer is not an essential tool, I include it here because if one is acquired, it would be most frustrating not to be able to read it (*see* Fig 3.25). The micrometer is operated by a screw of known pitch being turned a known number of times. The pitch of this screw is 40 threads per inch (TPI) on an imperial micrometer . This gives a travel of 0.025in for every complete turn, and 0.001in for every twenty-fifth part of a turn. The number of turns can be read from a simple scale numbered 0, 1, 2, etc., at each fourth division: each number indicates 0.1in (4 x 0.025). Parts of a complete turn are recorded by 25 graduations around the thimble, each marking a successive thousandth of an inch. These graduations are numbered at every fifth mark. The measurement is then indicated by the sum of three readings. This is best illustrated by taking the readings from Fig 3.24.

(i)	Two numbered turns (tenths)	0.200
(ii)	One other turn completely visible (fortieth)	0.025
(iii)	Seventeen sleeve divisions (thousandths)	0.017
Total		0.242

principle. It is able to measure $\frac{1}{1000}$in (*see* Diagram II). The fixed part is graduated in fortieths (0.025in), every fourth division being numbered, e.g. .1, .2, .3, etc. The slide has 25 divisions, occupying in all ⁶⁄₁₀in, so that each vernier division is 0.6 divided by 25, or 0.024in – one-thousandth shorter than each fixed division.

Whole numbers, tenths, fortieths, and then thousandths are read in order. Diagram II thus shows:

(i)	Whole numbers	0.00
(ii)	Tenths (seven)	0.70
(iii)	Fortieths (one)	0.025
(iv)	Thousandths (first line opposite is 0)	0.00
Total		0.725

Inside measurements are taken by using the outer surfaces of the jaws, which are slightly rounded to fit inside curved surfaces. As each jaw is 0.125in wide, then 0.25 must be added to all internal readings.

SURFACE PLATE AND SURFACE TABLE

Engineers do not mark out metal the way woodworkers set out their work – in woodwork the first task is to prepare the face side and face edge, and then mark from this data; metalwork, however, is marked from a surface that is not part of the job, a difficult concept for a woodworker to grasp.

The setting out involves the use of a perfectly flat surface, the surface plate or table. This is an expensive item and takes up quite a bit of space – for the woodworking toolmaker, the cost is not warranted, and therefore some flat surface must be contrived. A good piece of blockboard about 2ft square with plate glass on it will be ample.

THE SURFACE GAUGE OR SCRIBING BLOCK

From the plane of reference provided by the surface plate, measurements are transferred to the workpiece by the surface gauge. As it is difficult to mark out accurately without a surface gauge, one will be required. This tool has a scriber with a means of setting it a specific height above the surface plate. The scriber is set to height from a rule held

vertically above the plate. The combination square is ideal for this task, as the square head supports the rule, leaving the hands free to hold the workpiece and operate the gauge.

As well as its function as a marking out tool, the surface gauge is also used to test the size of parts being made. There are two dowels that are a push-fit in holes in the base of the gauge, which are used to scribe lines parallel to an edge very similar to a woodworker's marking gauge.

OTHER SPECIAL TOOLS

There are many other metalworking tools that might be useful, but it is quite easy to manage without them (*see* Fig 3.26). If you are fortunate and come by some of them, they will make the job in hand a little easier to do. Some are illustrated and briefly described as various techniques are discussed in other chapters, but the reader should not regard them as essential.

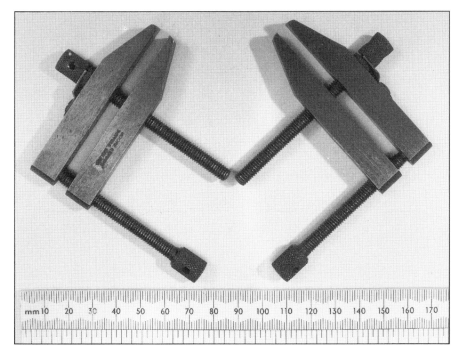

Fig 3.26 Toolmakers' clamps are very useful, and are to be preferred to G cramps for this type of work.

The Workshop

THE BENCH

It is assumed that anyone wishing to make woodworking tools will already have a reasonably equipped workshop set up for woodwork. There are some precautions that must be taken when performing metalworking tasks in that environment, as metal swarf (shavings and filings) can contaminate wood surfaces.

The bench used for metalwork will very soon become useless for woodwork unless certain precautions are taken. A false bench top should be made: this can be a piece of any old scrap sheet material which completely covers the whole surface of the bench. It is a good idea to make the top slightly bigger than the bench, with a batten screwed around its underside edges; by fitting around the edge of the bench, the batten stops the false top from moving about and prevents bits of metal from getting underneath it.

Fig 4.1 Engineers' vice bolted to a block of wood.

THE VICE

Under no circumstances use the woodwork bench vice for metalwork. There are two reasons: first, the wooden jaw linings would soon be ruined, and second, it is unsuitable for metalwork. The best approach to solving the problem is to bolt a block of wood to the metalwork vice and hold the block in the wood vice (*see* Fig 4.1). The working height required for the vice should be adjusted to make the top of the jaws level with the elbow.

The metalwork vice is fitted with hardened, serrated steel jaws – for much work these will need some form of softening fitted or they will badly mark the surface of the workpiece (*see* Fig 4.2). Proprietary fibre vice clamps are sold by tool shops for this purpose (*see* Fig 4.3), but they can be easily improvised (*see* Fig 4.4).

A screw clamp for holding threaded parts without damage should be made before it is needed, using Fig 4.5 as a reference: otherwise there is a great temptation to clamp a threaded part in the vice jaws, rather than stopping to make a screw clamp when it is required.

Fig 4.3 (right) Fibre softening pads.

Fig 4.2 Vice fitted with softening pads.

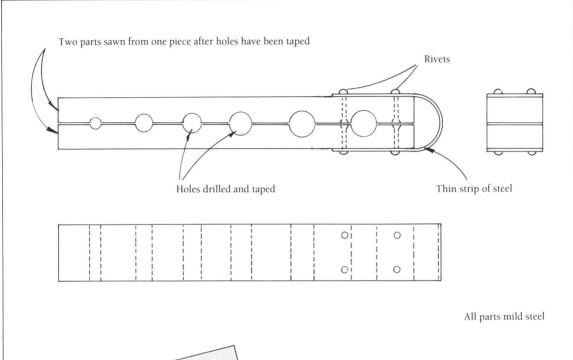

Two parts sawn from one piece after holes have been taped

Rivets

Holes drilled and taped

Thin strip of steel

All parts mild steel

Fig 4.5 *Clamp for holding threaded parts.*

Fig 4.4 *Installing softening pads in vice.*

instance, a coarse stone is needed for fast removal of material.

There is a safety factor to consider here. If the grinder runs at speeds around 3000 rpm, use wheels no larger than 6in in diameter, and make sure that the proper paper or lead washers are fitted at the sides of the wheel. It goes without saying that the spindle must be a good fit in the hole at the centre of the stone. Why all this palaver? Grinding stones can fly to pieces if unbalanced or damaged, causing nasty injuries.

THE GRINDER

Some form of grinding machine exists in most workshops. Unless it is solely for grinding woodcutting tools, it will probably fill a dual role by also grinding metal parts. There may be a need to fit different grades of wheel; for

DRILLING

There will be a lot of holes to drill, so some form of mechanisation is a must. There are very few workshops today that are not equipped with an electric drill. This is the minimum requirement – a press to hold the electric drill is a big improvement, and a pillar drill is luxury. It is very difficult to drill perpendicular to the surface by hand or with a hand-held electric drill, and there will be numerous times when you will need to do just that (*see* Fig 4.6).

HEAT

The woodworker is unlikely to already have anything that he can adapt or modify to fill the need for some means of raising metal to bright red heat. The ideal thing is an old, outdoor portable riveting forge; these are to be found secondhand, but not very often. So we have to make do with bottled gas with a fairly large torch – it might be more convenient and cleaner, but is not half the fun of a real live forge (*see* Fig 4.7).

THE GAS BURNER

These burners operate on propane or butane bottled gas. The main manufacturer is Primus-Sievert, and all major toolshops stock them. The burner requires a pressure of around 28psi, and the best way to make sure the pressure is correct is to use the regulator supplied by the burner manufacturer.

There are a number of different sizes of burners, the burner being a jet with a surrounding cone. A burner holder will be required; this is the handle part that contains the control valve. I find that a 3031 holder with a 2944 burner is the most useful. There are always comprehensive instructions with the parts, and they are very easy to set up and to use.

THE QUENCHING BATH

A container to hold the quenching liquid will be needed. A bucket will do, but is a bit on the small side. The ideal receptacle would be

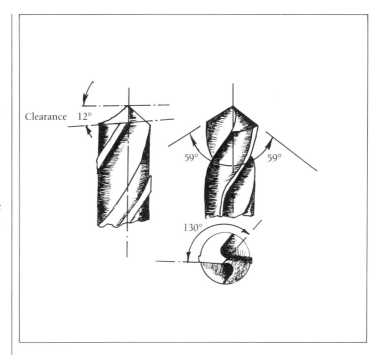

Fig 4.6 Angles on a twist drill.

Fig 4.7 Sievert gas torches.

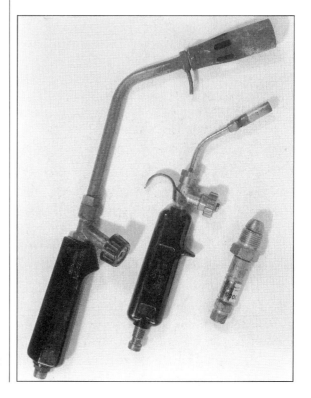

rectangular, about 9in wide, 18in long and 15in deep. I do not like having fire and water in my workshop, so all heat treatment is done in a shed at the bottom of the garden.

SAFETY

Unlike wood, metal presents several hazards of which the user should be aware. There are certain precautions that are only common sense – metal can be heavy, sharp and hot (*see* Fig 4.8). Eye protection should be worn most of the time, so a good pair of safety glasses is needed. You only have one pair of eyes – protect them, they cannot be replaced.

Heavy, sharp pieces of metal dropped on to the toes can do untold damage, while sharp pieces of steel swarf on the floor will penetrate the soles of some shoes. Safety footwear is not expensive, and is obligatory in most industrial workshops.

When handling metal that might be sharp or hot, use a good pair of industrial gloves. I speak from experience, as in my foolhardy younger days I had several nasty accidents; my wife has twice had to rush me to the hospital for stitches. There were numerous other stupid occurrences, until I learnt that accidents are not just things that happen to other people.

FIRE PRECAUTIONS

There should be a good quality fire extinguisher by the exit from the workshop. Why the exit? You need to fight fire from a position where you can get away from it should it get out of control, and the last thing you need in an emergency is to be trapped.

BETTER THINGS TO COME

I have told you about all the nasty things: how you will have to spend money on tools and other items, and what catastrophes may

Fig 4.8 Safety gear when handling hot metal: flameproof overalls, safety boots, welders gloves, safety glasses and hat.

happen in the workshop. Having got all that out of the way, we can now get down to the actual making.

Techniques

NEW SKILLS

When one starts to use a new skill, there will be a period at the start when the results may be discouraging. However, providing that the learner perseveres and does not give up, each successive task will build that individual skill: the more manual skills are used, the more adept the user becomes.

MARKING OUT

The accurate marking out of parts to be made from metal is fundamental to all the processes that will be used to make woodworking tools. Great care should be taken over accuracy; 'measure twice and cut once' is a good maxim.

A **scriber**, made from hardened tool steel with a sharply ground tip, will mark a fine line on metal (*see* Fig 5.1). The line is not always

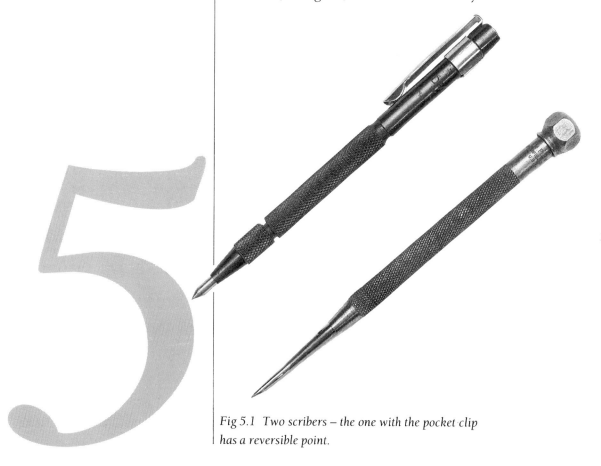

Fig 5.1 Two scribers – the one with the pocket clip has a reversible point.

Fig 5.2 Coating surface of metal with setting out blue prior to marking.

Fig 5.3 Surface gauge and rule stand on a small surface plate, setting the scriber in the gauge to an exact height.

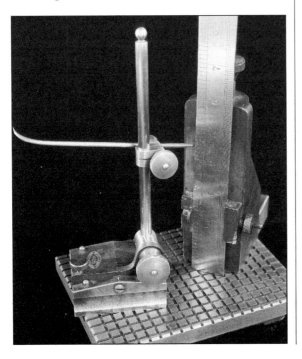

easy to see, but the surface of the metal can be coated with a fast-drying blue setting out lacquer (*see* Fig 5.2). The bare metal lines cut with the scriber stand out sharply against the blue. A good substitute for this lacquer is thin shellac polish that has been coloured with some aniline dye.

The hardened rule from a combination set is the ideal tool to use with the scriber to mark a straight line (*see* Fig 5.3). When filing metal down to a line, the line becomes very difficult to work to as the last small amount of metal is removed. This problem is overcome by enhancing the scribed line with a series of fine indentations about ¼in apart along its length. The tool used for this is the dot punch, or an automatic centre punch that has had its point ground to a fine angle (*see* Fig 5.4).

Once a straight flat surface has been worked on a part, all further setting out is done off the surface plate. Flat metal is best stood against some support that will hold it square to the plate's surface. Lines are then scribed on its surface using the surface gauge. This process is best explained by illustration, and Figs 5.5 and 5.6 show this technique as it would be applied to different marking tasks. The point of the surface gauge scriber is set from a rule that has been stood up perpendicular to the surface plate (*see* Fig 5.7).

USING THE HACKSAW

When cutting with the hacksaw, the correct stance and grip are essential. The hacksaw is held with both hands, one each end of the frame. The index finger of the hand on the handle is extended along the side of the frame to control direction (*see* Fig 5.8). Metal to be cut should be held securely – if it is in the vice, the line to be cut should be placed as near to the jaws as practicable. Wherever possible,

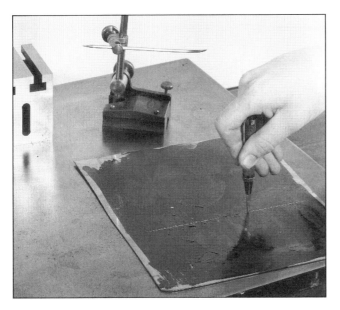

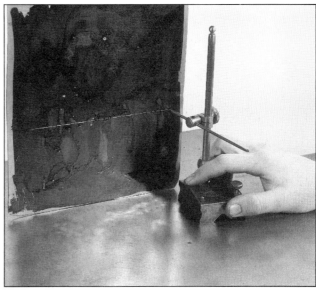

Fig 5.4 (above left) Using an automatic centre punch to enhance a previously scribed line.

Fig 5.5 (above right) Scribing line with surface gauge.

Fig 5.6 (left) Scribing a line using a vernier height gauge – more accurate than a surface gauge, but more expensive.

Fig 5.7 (below) Setting the scriber height.

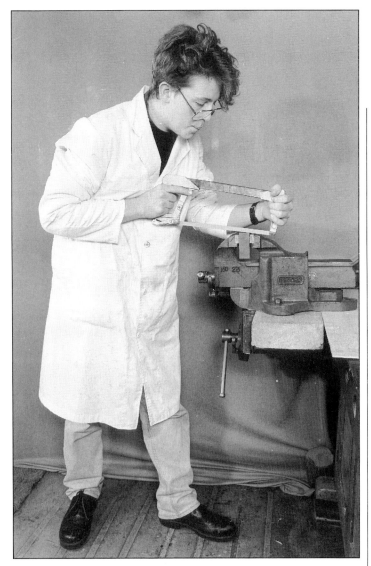

Fig 5.8 Correct stance and hand positions for hacksawing.

the job over and cut from the other side.

Try to have at least three teeth in contact with the metal; less than this puts strain on the individual tooth, which breaks off. It is good practice to make a small nick with a file when starting a cut, as this allows several teeth to start the cut. Starting a saw on the corner of the metal without a file nick means one tooth takes all the shock of knocking the corner off.

FILING

It is not easy to acquire the art of filing a surface true. However, there are some basic rules which, if observed, will help considerably. The work should be held firmly in the vice, with the surface to be filed horizontal (see Fig 5.9). Keep the work low down in the vice, with the surface to be worked as near the jaws as possible. The file handle is grasped in the right hand as shown in Fig 5.10. The left hand, which is used to apply pressure to the end of the file, may be placed in different positions, depending on the task in hand – for heavy work where a good deal of metal is being removed, the position would be totally different to that when a fine finishing cut is being made. These different positions are illustrated in Figs 5.10 and 5.11.

Stance and balance play an important part in filing. Body weight is transferred from one foot to the other with every stroke of the file. There must be no reliance on the arms in keeping the balance, or the file will reflect those forces employed. The stroke is made keeping the right forearm horizontal and the elbow tucked in close to the body. The body sways a little as the stroke proceeds, and weight is transferred from the right to the left

place the metal so that the cut is vertical.

Use the full length of the blade, not just the centre part. Failure to do this will result in the set wearing from the centre only, and at some stage the wider set at the ends of the blade will jam in the cut and the blade will break.

The speed of cut should be a regular 50 strokes a minute; resist all temptation to cut faster than this. If cutting cast steel, reduce the cutting rate to 30 strokes or less per minute. Too much pressure on the blade must be avoided, as this not only shortens blade life, but also makes the cut wander from the straight line. If a blade breaks, do not try to follow in the cut with a new blade, but turn foot, the aim being to keep the file truly horizontal throughout all of the stroke (*see* Fig 5.12).

When **cross-filing**, the file moves from left to right as well as back and forth. A speed of 50 to 60 strokes per minute should not be exceeded, and only half this speed should be used on cast steel.

Which file to use depends on the job in hand. The usual procedure is to start with the big coarse files and work down to the smaller finer ones. If work has been marked out with a dot punch as previously described, filing proceeds until the dot marks break through the surface being worked.

Draw-filing is a finishing process where the file is held at right angles to the work and worked sideways to normal cross-filing. The file normally used will be a fine one, as the purpose of draw-filing is to remove the marks

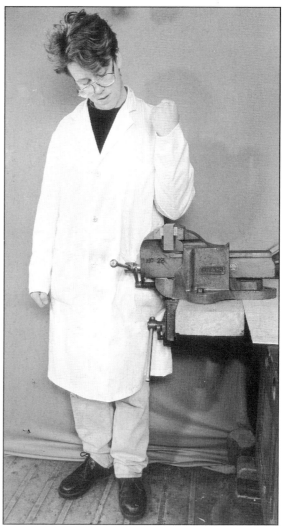

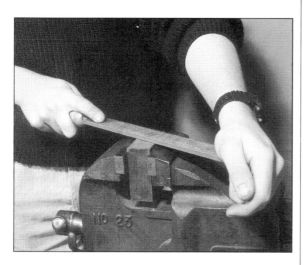

Fig 5.9 (top right) The correct height of a metalworking vice – elbow height.

Fig 5.10 (above) Holding the file to remove the maximum amount of metal.

Fig 5.11 (right) Correct hand position for filing accurately.

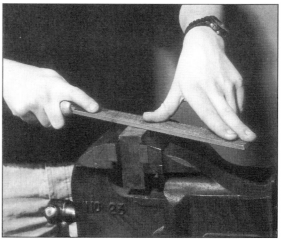

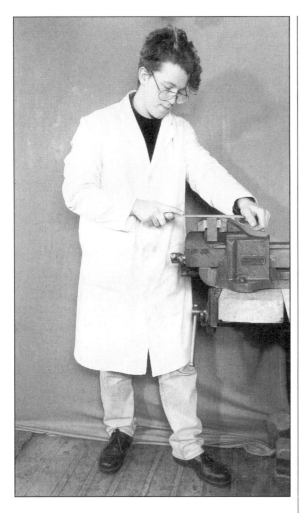

made by cross-filing. The grip used on the file is important: the index fingers should be on top of the file and over the surface being filed (*see* Fig 5.13). It will be found that the sharpest part of a file is up near the tang – this is an ideal part to use for draw-filing.

There is a tendency when filing to work the surface slightly rounded, and therefore good files are slightly convexed in their length. When filing, frequent checks should be made to see if the surface is flat and square. This checking should not be left until the setting out line is reached, for if the edge is out of square the wrong way, this will be too late.

SCRAPING

The goal when scraping is to produce a flat surface. The edge of the scraper must be ground sharp and finished on an oilstone, and the surface to be scraped must first have the high spots marked on it. This is done by coating the surface plate with a thin even coat of engineers' blue, a greasy substance with blue pigment in it. The surface to be marked is wiped clean and rubbed on the blued surface plate; the high spots will now be marked blue. These high spots are all scraped off, using the scraper at approximately 45° to the centre line of the workpiece. The job is wiped clean and rubbed on to the blued surface plate again. This time, the blue high spots are scraped off using the scraper at 90° to the centre line. This procedure is continued, altering the angle that the work is scraped at each time until about 75% of the surface blues up, or the surface is considered flat enough.

Fig 5.12 (top) Correct stance for filing.

Fig 5.13 Position of hands when draw filing.

DRILLING HOLES

In terms of skill, this is probably the most underrated task. Much time will be spent drilling holes, and most must be in the correct position and of the correct size. The condition of the drill will affect both criteria. Because certain sizes of drill will be used a considerable amount, they will become blunt, which means they will have to be sharpened.

There are many proprietary jigs and attachments that can be obtained to help in this task, but I have yet to find one that works 100%. There is nothing that will compare with the skill of a competent craftsman who can do the job on a bench grinder freehand, and it is worth practising until you have this skill.

The problem is knowing just what is required to produce a good cutting tip to a drill. The tip of a standard twist drill is ground with an included angle of 118°, suitable for general work. The cutting lip needs some clearance for most common usage, when the chisel edge at the centre of the drill has an angle of 130° with the cutting edge. Keep your drills sharp, and when any dullness is suspected, stop work and sharpen the drill (*see* Fig 5.14).

When a hole is needed in an exact position, it is not good enough just to mark its centre; a square the size of the hole should be marked. When the drill has cut a dimple in the surface of the work, the work should be inspected. It is very easy to see if the drill is working in the correct position in the centre of the square. If there is any inaccuracy, the centre of the dimple will need drawing to the position where it should be with a half-round cold chisel. (*See* Fig 5.15 for the position for removing metal with a cold chisel.)

Use the correct cutting fluid for the material being drilled: soluble oil for steels, and paraffin for aluminium. (Cast iron, brass

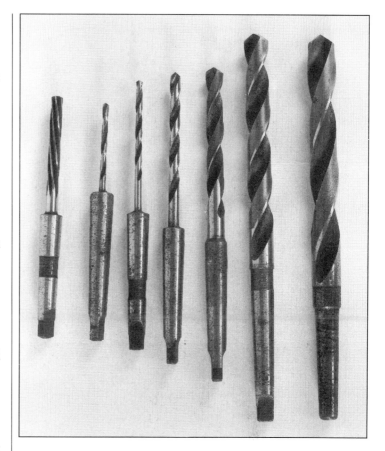

Fig 5.14 (top) Drills with Morse taper shanks are best for use in pillar drill. Note the reamer on the left.

Fig 5.15 Removing metal with a cold chisel.

and phosphor bronze are drilled dry.) Do not allow the flutes of the drill to become choked up with swarf, particularly when drilling deep holes.

Ease the pressure on the drill as it breaks through, or the uneven cutting action may well break it. The drill must be kept cutting, and must never be allowed to just rub, as this builds up heat, which spoils the cutting edge.

Straight shank drills must be held tightly in the chuck; if they are allowed to slip, the shank of the drill is spoilt. This not only results in difficulty in reading the drill's size, but may make the drill run out of true.

Work to be drilled should be firmly secured, both to ensure accurate drilling and for safety's sake – a drill snatching a piece of metal can revolve it at the same speed as that at which the drill is turning. Where parts have to be cut from the plate, such as sides for a plane, the easiest way is to drill a series of holes around the periphery of the part. These holes should be as near one another as is practically possible, and can then be joined up with an Abra file.

The Abra file is a round blade which looks very much like a piece of wire. It is held in a hacksaw frame, and there are special adapters

Fig 5.16 Taps, showing different sizes and threads.

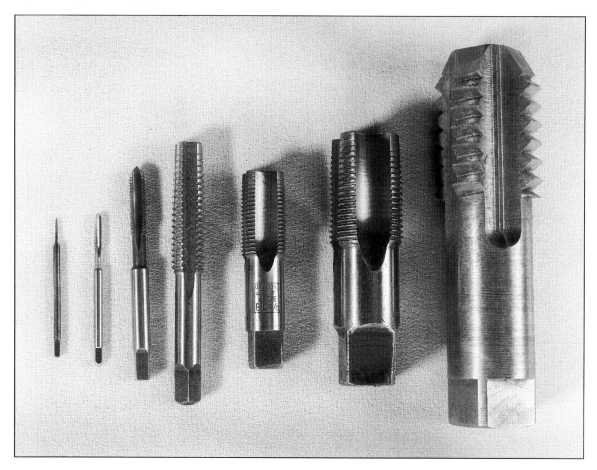

to hold the ends to the pins on the frame. An Abra file is used in much the same way as the hacksaw but, being round, cuts in any direction.

CUTTING THREADS

When cutting an internal thread, it is important that the hole drilled to receive the thread is of the correct size. This is known as the tapping size; tool shops sell sets of tables that give the drill size for each thread (*see* Fig 5.16). If the hole is undersize, the chances are that the tap will be broken off. (It is wise when buying taps to also purchase the correct size drill, which can then be kept with the taps, ensuring that the correct size will always be at hand.)

Retrieving the part of the broken tap that remains in the hole is a problem. Various methods are suggested in engineering textbooks, but I have never had much success with any of them. Probably the best maxim is to be very careful not to break the tap in the first place!

Having drilled the hole, take the taper tap and fix the tap wrench to it (*see* Fig 5.17). Tighten up the wrench so that it will not work loose in operation. Enter the tap into the hole,

Fig 5.17 *Selection of tap wrenches.*

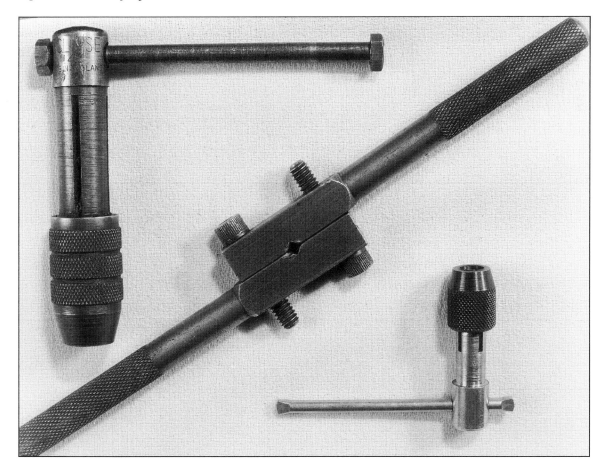

taking great care to keep the tap in line with the drilled hole and square to the surface. Turn the tap forwards and then backwards – the backwards turn is to break the shaving and ease the next cut forwards. Some form of cutting oil will be needed on all metals except cast iron and brass – the value of cutting oil has to be experienced to be appreciated.

If the tapping hole has been drilled with a pillar drill, leave the job on the machine table and replace the drill with a tap. Enter the tap into the hole and turn the drill quill back and forth to start the tap. This procedure ensures that the hole is tapped true. The procedure

adopted when tapping blind holes is to replace the taper tap with the second tap when it reaches the bottom of the hole; this in turn is replaced by the plug tap. It is necessary to clean the swarf from the bottom of the hole periodically to give the tap working room.

Dies can be obtained in several different types, and the split die is best for our purpose (*see* Fig 5.18). The split in the die permits limited adjustment to the size of the thread being cut. The recessed part of the stocks into which the die fits contains three screws with pointed ends. The centre screw fits into the split in the die.

Fig 5.18 Stocks and dies. Note the three grub screws in the larger stock and the three dimples in the die stood on edge. The large die is a nut die, used only to clean up a damaged thread.

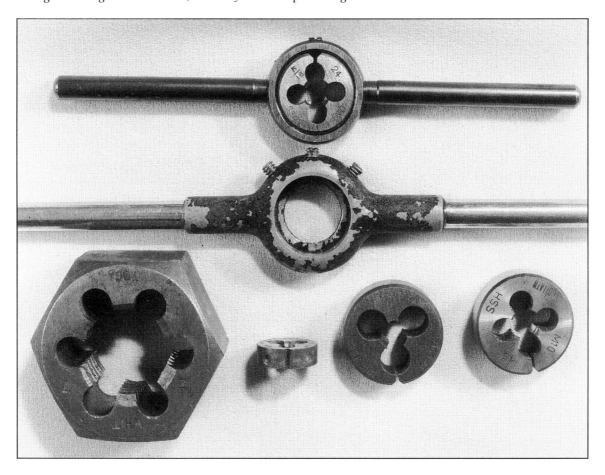

If the two outer screws are left loose and the centre one tightened, the die is expanded to its largest size. Conversely, if the centre screw is left loose and the outer two screws tightened, closing the split, then the die is set to its smallest size. The die size may be set anywhere between these two extremes by adjustment of the three screws.

The technique used to cut an external thread is very similar to that employed when forming an internal one with a tap. If the die is inspected, it will be seen that the threads are chamfered away on one face – this is the side of the die presented to the work first.

There is some difficulty in making sure that the die is started squarely on the end of the bar to be threaded. Only the first two threads are chamfered, and this does not give much assistance in keeping the die square at the beginning.

Before presenting the die to the end of the bar, open the die with the centre screw, so that the first cut will be shallow. Follow this cut with the die closed down to size. In this way the thread size can be adjusted to fit the internal thread into which it will screw. For this reason, internal threads are always cut first. Remember to use a suitable cutting compound or oil, and reverse the die stocks about every half turn, to break the shaving and clear the swarf.

If the thread has to be cut right up to a bolt head or a projection, the thread is first cut in the normal way, and then the die is reversed in the stocks and run back on the thread previously cut. This will cut the last two shallow threads to their full depth.

SOFT SOLDERING

There are a number of soft solders on the market. The type that we are interested in for our purpose is generally known as **tinman's**
solder. This is an alloy of tin, lead and antimony, and is usually sold in sticks just over 1ft long and of a triangular section. The type sold for electronic use, which looks like wire on a reel, can be used in an emergency, although its composition is not formulated for our purpose. British Standard 219 lists solders: the two that we are interested in are 219/C, with 40% tin, 57.8% lead, 2.2% antimony; and 219/K, with 60% tin, 39.5% lead, 0.5% antimony, the latter being more useful.

Solder reacts with the parent metal to form an amalgam; this is the case with most metals, the main exception being aluminium, which needs a special solder. For the union to take place between the metal surfaces and the solder, the metals must be scrupulously clean – molten solder dropped on to an unclean surface will form into a ball, like water on a hot metal surface. Cleaning should be done with a file or wire wool; emery or other abrasive paper can sometimes be used, but is not to be recommended because particles of the abrasive come loose from the base and remain embedded in the surface, which can stop the solder from adhering properly.

No matter how clean the surface, when heated it will react with the oxygen in the air and the surface will oxidize. A flux must be used to stop this chemical action taking place. There are two basic types of flux: one protects the clean surface and prevents oxidization, while the other performs these tasks and also helps clean the surface. The latter is sold under the trade name of Baker's Fluid, and is in fact zinc chloride, made by dissolving zinc in hydrochloric acid. This flux, whilst highly efficient, is also very corrosive, and any work where it is used must be scrubbed clean once the soldering is finished. The fumes also seem to turn any ferrous metal in the vicinity rusty. The other type of flux has very little cleaning

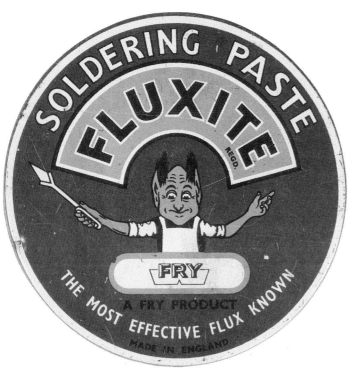

Fig 5.19 Fluxite.

property, but is much kinder to use, being based on resin and petroleum jelly: the best known brand is Fluxite (*see* Fig 5.19).

A soldering iron is used for most work, 'iron' being a misnomer, as the bit is always made of copper. Before use the iron's bit is cleaned and tinned with a thin coating of solder. This is very easily done by cleaning the heated bit with an old file, dipping it in flux, and then applying solder to it. The hot bit covered with molten solder is then wiped on an old rag, and this leaves the working end covered in an even layer of solder.

The size of iron is matched to the job, and several sizes will be necessary. I find that where a big iron is needed, the type that is heated in a gas flame is best. With the smaller irons, an electrical type is more convenient. Soft solder is not used very much in the making of tools; the main purpose to which it will be put is sweating steel soles on to gunmetal planes.

The sweating procedure, adapted for putting a steel sole on to a nonferrous metal plane, is as follows: both the plate of steel and the underside of the plane casting are first 'tinned' – the process of running a thin film of solder over the entire surface. The two tinned surfaces are placed together and the whole assembly is heated – if the plane casting is supported upside down on two fire bricks, a gas torch can be played underneath the assembly to heat it up. When the solder is seen to be free running, the steel sole will seem to float on the molten solder. The torch is then removed and pressure applied to the sole by two metal bars held in the hands.

The solder will take some time to solidify; cold air blown over the job will help, but under no circumstances splash cold water on it, as the sudden cooling from being doused with water can seriously damage the casting. The secret of a well-made soldered joint is that the solder line is kept very thin, the optimum thickness being 0.003in. A thicker layer will not be as strong, and will mar the appearance of the finished item.

HARD SOLDERS AND BRAZING STRIP

Although there is no real demarcation line between hard solders and brasses, an approximate division can be made as follows: hard solders melt from 400° to 750° centigrade, while brazing strip has a higher working temperature of 750° to 1083° centigrade. Because of the much higher temperatures involved, these alloys cannot be worked with an iron as that used for soft solder. A gas burner or blowtorch is the most convenient method of raising the work to the required temperature.

I find that Easy-flo No 2 works well as a hard solder suitable for general use. It is an alloy of 42% silver, 17% copper, 16% zinc and

25% cadmium, with a melting range of 608° to 617° centigrade, and complies with British Standard Spec. 1854 AG2. A flux will be needed – I can recommend Easy-flo flux. It is manufactured to complement the solder, and is to be recommended.

If there is a need for brazing (though this rarely occurs when making woodworking tools), a means of obtaining fairly high temperatures will be needed. The Primus-Sievert gas burner mentioned in Chapter 4 will do, if it is large enough. A big part being worked on will absorb a lot of heat lost by radiation – to prevent this, the job can be packed in a fireproof insulating material, leaving only the part to be worked on exposed. A word of warning – make sure that the melting point of the part being brazed is higher than that of the brazing strip.

When hard soldering or brazing, the surfaces to be joined should be scrupulously clean and smeared with paste flux: borax is the usual flux used when brazing. A small quantity is mixed into a paste with water, for coating the surfaces to be joined. The hot end of the rod of solder or brass is then dipped into the powdered flux, which adheres to the rod. The heat melts the powder into the joint and prevents oxidization. When the joint is completed and allowed to cool down, it will be found that the molten flux has solidified into a hard black glassy substance that will need to be removed, either by chipping it off mechanically or by pickling. Pickling involves immersing the work in a sulphuric acid and water bath. The proportions for this are 1 part concentrated sulphuric acid to 10 parts of water. **Add the acid to the water**, not the water to the acid, but even so, pour the acid into the water very slowly and carefully, as the mixing of the two liquids causes considerable heat, and the mass of water will absorb this. If the water is added to the acid, the heat produced will cause the mix to boil and raw acid will be thrown out of the mixing vessel. Even the diluted mix is dangerous – it will burn holes in clothes etc., and should be used with caution.

RIVETING

Riveting can be considered as a permanent method of joining metal parts together; it is equivalent to nailing in woodwork. As far as the manufacture of woodworking tools is concerned, it is only used in one or two cases: the sides of the British steel plane are riveted, as is the swivel on the Norris blade adjuster. This work is carried out cold and is explained in full in the detailed instructions for making those parts in Chapters 13 and 15.

Heat Treatment

WHY HEAT-TREAT METAL?

'Heat treatment' is a general term describing the various processes used to change the physical properties of a metal by subjecting it to heat. Both ferrous and nonferrous metals can to some extent have their properties changed by heat treatment. Most metals work-harden under the compressive strain of repeated hammering or bending, and may be brought to a softer and more manageable state by annealing. Copper and its alloys may be annealed by raising them to a dull red heat and then quenching in water, or allowing them to cool in the air. Aluminium is annealed in a similar way, but is heated to a much lower temperature because it will melt before reaching a visible heat.

STRUCTURE OF STEEL

It is with steel that most of the heat treatment processes will be carried out. With the appropriate treatment, various grades of steel can be made to cover the whole range of properties that will be required; these properties will be affected according to the carbon content of the steel (*see* Chapter 2).

When carbon steel is heated, its temperature rises at a uniform rate until it reaches 700°C – at this point the temperature remains constant for a short time, before rising at a slower rate until it reaches 800°C, above which the temperature rises at the original rate.

When the metal is allowed to cool, this procedure is reversed. The point at which the temperature pause occurs when heating the metal is called the decalescence point. The point at which the temperature remains stationary when cooling is called the recalescence point. Decalescence and recalescence occur at the lower critical point of the steel, the point at which the structure of the steel begins to change. This structural change continues until the steel is heated to its upper critical point, which varies according to the carbon content of the steel.

If the steel is allowed to cool naturally, the internal structure of the steel reverts to its original state. If, however, the rate of cooling is properly increased or decreased, the internal structure of the steel will remain permanently changed.

ANNEALING STEEL

The object of annealing is to make the steel as soft and ductile as possible, and therefore make it easier to work. This is achieved by heating the workpiece to its hardening temperature, holding it at that temperature long enough to reach an even temperature throughout and then allowing it to cool as slowly as possible. This slow rate of cooling is most important – where a furnace is used, the steel is left inside after the heat is turned off, and the whole is allowed to cool down. I frequently use a blowtorch to heat my metal: when it has been heated long enough, I bury it in a box of fine ash. (My workshop is heated by a solid fuel boiler that will also burn sawdust and planer chips.) I also put metal into the boiler's firebox, where it is heated to cherry red, and I then transfer it to cool slowly in an ash pit.

NORMALIZING STEEL

Normalizing is a process used to relieve stresses set up in the steel by working it, or to put the steel back to its normal condition after incorrect heat treatment. The procedure for normalizing is similar to that used to anneal steel, except that the steel is allowed to cool normally in the atmosphere.

Engineers who are constantly heat-treating metal use sophisticated apparatus such as pyrometers to enable the temperature to be accurately controlled. The blacksmiths who originally made the woodworker's tools had none of these refinements; I have made tools relying purely on my own eyesight to judge the temperature of the metal, with excellent results. So do not worry if you feel you know nothing about steel; you will learn when you work and practice, as I did.

It is much easier to judge the colour of the metal when heating it if you work in subdued lighting. The first perceivable colour is dark red; this occurs at around 700°C. As the temperature rises the red becomes brighter, reaching cherry red at about 830°C and bright cherry at 900°C. Unless you are fortunate and own a forge, it will be very difficult to obtain temperatures much above this point, but it is quite adequate for heat treatment, if insufficient for forging.

HARDENING STEEL

Hardening is carried out by heating to a cherry red and then cooling suddenly (quenching). There is no point in overheating the steel, and in fact this should be avoided, as it coarsens the crystalline structure.

QUENCHING

Water is the universal medium for most work. It is best if the water is warm, as cold water can cause fine cracks in the surface of the steel being treated. I am told that some steels harden better in brine, but have not tried this treatment. Brine is a saturated solution of rock salt in water, and has a higher boiling point than water. Using old sump oil seems to impart a different characteristic to the steel, which I can best explain as toughness. Oil is useful for fine and delicate things that distort when cooled in water, but I have seldom used it, as plain water seems to work for all my

Fig 6.1 *Steel being quenched in water.*

from the cooling effect of the quenching medium.

TEMPERING

Hardened steel is brittle and requires some degree of toughness restored to it before it is suitable for most purposes – this is done by tempering, which involves reheating the metal to a point well below decalescence and then quenching it.

It is fairly easy to tell the temperature of the metal when tempering, by polishing the metal to a bright surface. As the metal is heated this surface will oxidize, and the oxidation colour will change as the temperature rises. The first colour to appear is a faint straw, which becomes darker until it finally reaches a deep blue.

The application of heat when tempering needs very careful control. The gas torch is suitable if the workpiece is kept well out of the flame. Once the colours start running along the steel, things can happen very fast, so be prepared. When tempering small items, I have a ¼in thick steel plate on two bricks; the torch is played on the underside of the plate, and the item being tempered is kept on the top side.

When tempering cutting tools such as chisels and plane irons, heat is applied to the opposite end to that which will be sharpened. The colours can be seen to run down the blade to the cutting edge.

The colour that you temper to will, of course, depend on the use to which the cutting edge will be put. I suggest that you err on the hard side, as the tool can then be re-tempered to make it softer. If it is too soft, it will have to be rehardened. For bench work

needs. Oil and red-hot steel is an invitation for a fire to start, so have a suitable extinguisher handy if you decide to use oil.

There is a technique that should be followed when quenching: the work should be plunged vertically into the bath, and then kept moving about (*see* Fig 6.1). Work must never be held still during quenching, as a barrier of vapour can build up around it and insulate it on fine cabinetmaking, I find that the slightest suspicion of light straw at the cutting edge suits me fine.

I would suggest that if you are a newcomer to heat treatment, you get some old bits of high carbon steel and experiment with them; you will soon find that a lot of the mystique disappears from the subject.

CASE-HARDENING

Mild steel cannot be hardened by heating and quenching, due to the low content of carbon contained in it. However, the carbon content of the outer surface can be increased by heating the component to be treated to a cherry red, and plunging it into a substance rich in carbon. The still red-hot part is then quenched in water. Because the outer skin of the part is rich in carbon it becomes very hard, while the inner core retains the characteristics of mild steel. This treatment is ideal for the parts of plane adjusters that take a good deal of wear. I use Kasenit, a proprietary product for case-hardening, obtainable from most engineers' suppliers (see Fig 6.2). Full instructions are printed on the tin.

MEASURING THE HARDNESS

There are several different systems for specifying the hardness of metals. The main ones are: Vickers hardness number, Brinell, Rockwell 'B' and Rockwell 'C'. This last one is the system that most woodworking tool manufacturers work to; tables comparing one system to another are available.

Rockwell 'C' is the system used in this book. The hardness of the metal is determined by a machine which pushes a 120° diamond cone into the surface of the metal with a known force; the same machine measures the depth that the cone penetrates the metal – the deeper the indentation, the softer the metal.

When asking for a blade to be heat-treated for woodwork, I specify 61° Rockwell 'C'; with most high carbon steels this works out fine. Any higher and the blade is brittle, while anything lower than 58° Rockwell 'C' will be too soft.

Fig 6.2 Kasenit.

Pattern
Making

Fig 7.1 *Smoother made from a gun metal casting, with a sweated on sole.*

CASTING

Many of the tools that a woodworker may wish to make will involve metal parts of complex shape (*see* Fig 7.1). It would be a daunting task to try to cut these parts from a solid piece of material, but if molten metal is poured into a mould of the required shape, the part is produced in a form that only needs finishing. This process is called casting. The first step in producing a casting is to make a full-size model (pattern) of the item required; from this model a mould is produced, and for most items this will be in moulding sand.

MOULDING

Fortunately the castings we require are of a simple shape compared with most engineering castings (*see* Fig 7.2), but some knowledge of sand moulding is desirable if the patterns made are to produce good castings. Moulding is an exceedingly difficult and important process in metal casting. The foundry entrusted to produce the casting will also carry out the moulding. Moulding sand is fine sand mixed with a small percentage of clay, powdered charcoal and coal dust, or other ingredients, to give it the right consistency.

The sand is firmly rammed around the pattern, the whole contained in a box without a top or bottom, known as a **drag**. All the castings needed for our purpose have one face that is a flat plane. This surface is kept level with the top of the sand. When the sand has been rammed around the pattern so that it forms a solid, the pattern is removed.

Fig 7.2 Raw castings in bronze. Top, a body for a mitre plane. Below, left to right: five fences for a coachmakers' router, small router body.

Another box similar to the drag is prepared. This box, known as the **cope**, has sand rammed solid in it with two holes going right through, from top to bottom. One hole is used to pour the molten metal down and is called the 'pouring gate', the other smaller hole is known as the 'riser' and allows air to escape from the mould cavity, providing a head of molten metal. When the casting is of a large size, several additional small holes are made by inserting wires which, when removed, provide additional vents through which air can escape when the metal is being poured. The cope is placed on top of the drag, and forms a lid and upper part to the mould.

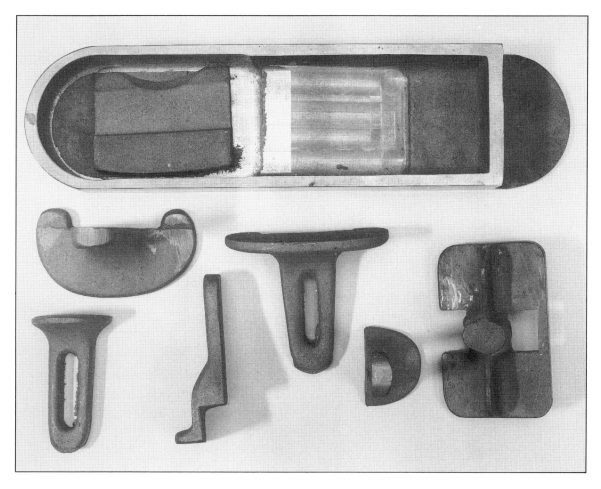

TAPER AND RAPPING PLATE

There are two important features that the moulder requires in a pattern. The first is the **taper**, which allows the pattern to be freely withdrawn from the sand without damaging the mould. A good average for this taper is ⅛in in 1ft. Any projections that would stop the mould being withdrawn must be made detachable on the pattern; these pieces can then be withdrawn after the main pattern has been removed from the sand. The moulder will also require a **rapping plate** fixed to the flat part of the pattern. This plate is a flat piece of metal with a ¼in hole in it. The rapping plate is housed flush with the surface of the pattern to which it is screwed. The moulder puts a spike in the hole, and by tapping the side of the spike the pattern is freed from the sand and can be withdrawn.

CONTRACTION

All castings contract in cooling from the molten state, so patterns have to be made correspondingly larger than the required casting. If, for example, a cast iron plate 1ft long was required, the pattern would have to be 1ft⅒in long. If the pattern is at all complicated, all the dimensions will have to be calculated – however, these calculations can be avoided by using a pattern maker's contraction rule. This usually has standard measurements on one face and the contraction for cast iron, brass and aluminium on the other three edges.

Fortunately most of the castings required for making woodworking tools are smallish, and the exact finished size can have a wide tolerance by engineering standards, so only critical dimensions need to have the contraction allowance. For general work, the usual agreed contractions are: cast iron ⅒in to 1ft, brass ⅛in to 1ft, aluminium ¼in to 1ft.

SETTING DOWN

Before attempting to make the pattern, a full-size drawing incorporating the contraction is made. Pattern makers refer to this as **setting down**. I find the best medium to set down on is hardboard that has been given a couple of coats of white emulsion paint. A hard pencil, say 4H sharpened to a chisel edge, will give a fine accurate line. The taper should be included in the drawing, so a decision on which way the part is to be moulded will need to be made beforehand. If any surfaces need an allowance of metal for machining or filing, this will be added to the dimensions when setting down.

MAKING THE PATTERN

Passing to the actual making of the pattern, it is crucial that a pattern should be constructed as strong as practicable, as it will be subjected to some rough usage in the foundry. It is also important to consider that the pattern will be in contact with damp moulding sand and stored in a dry storeroom, so a good deal of thought must be given to the method of construction.

The actual construction of the pattern is quite simple in woodworking terms: most joints are butted, glued and pinned or screwed, and all pinholes and screw heads must be filled and finished flush with the surface of the pattern (*see* Figs 7.3 and 7.4).

FILLETS

Internal angles are filled in with a fillet in all pattern work, as leaving a sharp internal corner on a pattern makes the mould very weak at such a corner. If a fillet is not fitted, there is a tendency for the flow of metal to wash the corner away and thus spoil the casting. It is therefore good practice to fill all corners to provide a stronger mould, which

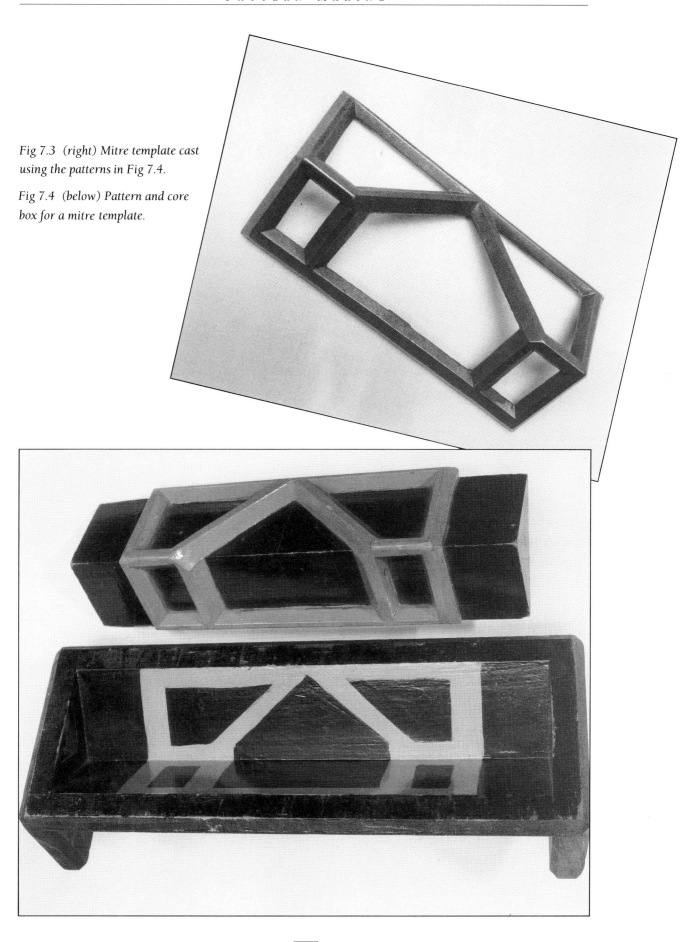

Fig 7.3 (right) Mitre template cast using the patterns in Fig 7.4.

Fig 7.4 (below) Pattern and core box for a mitre template.

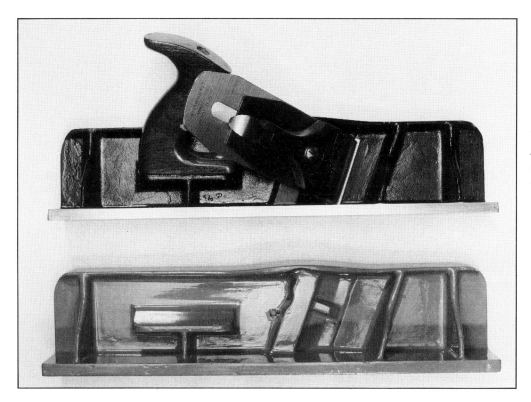

Fig 7.5 Pattern and the finished plane, which was cast in a mould made with the pattern.

also adds considerably to the strength and appearance of the finished casting.

There are several companies which will supply special fillet material to pattern makers; unfortunately the smallest quantity they will deliver is far too much for our requirements. Find a local firm that makes patterns, tell them what you are doing, and get them to sell you a few lengths. The best fillet material is leather strip with a triangular section: this strip can be stuck into the corner with PVA glue, and the leather rubbed into the corner with a small steel ball. This procedure forms the fillet into a clean radius. There is also a proprietary wax fillet that is fixed into the corner with a warm steel ball, though this is not as good as the leather.

THE FINISH

The surface of the pattern should be rubbed smooth with garnet paper; I find 220 grit is about right. Pattern makers use a coloured, spirit-based lacquer to finish the pattern. There is a colour code used in the trade: finished casting parts are coloured orange, surfaces with machine allowance are yellow, and cores and coreprints are black, but the latter need not concern us. Several coats are given, rubbed down between each coat, and then a final coat of clear lacquer is applied. While it is nice to make the pattern look professional, several coats of shellac brought to a good finish will satisfy most foundries (*see* Fig 7.5).

CASTING AND FOUNDRIES

Having made your pattern, you will need to find a foundry to mould and cast it. Start with the Yellow Pages, as it is best if you can find a foundry close to home. It helps if for the first couple of castings you can talk to the foundry manager – with smaller foundries, there is the chance that they will have an interest in what you are doing, and give constructive advice. Most foundries charge for castings by weight, and you may get a reduction in the charge if you have several castings made at the same time. The best advice I can give is to find a foundry that undertakes one-off castings, and go and talk to them.

The Technology of Planes

The most complicated tool the woodworker will make will be a plane. There are many things to be considered before even starting to design the proposed tool, so it is important that all the features influencing the way the finished plane will work are understood (*see* Fig 8.1). By considering the more important of these, we can be sure that, after spending a good deal of time constructing the tool, it will work the way we intended.

Obviously the first thing to decide is just what the proposed plane is to be. Broadly speaking, planes fall into several classifications; bench planes, such as fore planes, jack planes, smoothers etc., have many things in common, whereas shoulder planes, mitre planes, and thumb and chariot planes have features exclusive to that plane only.

WEIGHT

The first feature to consider – and this is applicable to all planes – is **weight**. This is where you can tailor the tool to your own individual preference; but don't overdo things. If you look at the tools most sought after, the reason for their popularity can quickly be perceived. When I was thinking about making my 30in copy of a Norris jointer, I was able to handle an original at the preview of an auction sale, and the heavy weight astounded me. I saved quite a lot of weight on mine by using walnut instead of rosewood to fill the plane, and by having recessed panels milled out inside the sole. Conversely, extra weight was required when I made my smoother – a thick gunmetal casting, to which a steel sole was fixed, was used for the body. Weight can therefore be built in or designed out.

THICKNESS OF CUTTING IRON

The thickness of the cutting iron can have some effect on how the plane works, and will also affect the size of the mouth aperture. A thin iron as fitted to Bailey pattern planes will save time in sharpening, but may well chatter when planing difficult wood. Norris fitted ⁵⁄₃₂in thick irons, which I consider the minimum. If all the effort of making a ridged, well-constructed plane is to be undertaken, then surely a little more time spent in sharpening is no great burden.

PITCH

The pitch of the iron has considerable influence on the way the plane works; the term 'pitch' refers to the angle made by the cutting iron and the sole of the plane. If we examine the planes used for planing along the grain, which are fitted with a back iron, and we imagine the wood fibres being magnified until they look like a bundle of straw, a plane iron with a very low angle will tend to split the straws apart, while an iron with a steep angle will scrape the fibres without splitting them.

The low-angled iron will require far less energy to make a cut than the steep iron. At one time, planes with a shallow pitch were referred to as softwood planes, and steep-pitched as hardwood planes. Most current mass-produced bench planes have a pitch of 45°, which is known as common or standard pitch. Smoothers made in years gone by to plane difficult hardwood had a pitch of 50°, known as York pitch. Thomas Norris compromised by making his bench planes with a pitch of 47.5°.

Cabinetmakers who worked difficult woods with easily torn curly grain made their own smoother; this tool would have a pitch as steep as 55°, called middle pitch. Moulding planes, with a single iron set with the bevel down, need to have a steep pitch to prevent the grain tearing out – some are as steep as 60°.

SINGLE-IRONED PLANES

When considering planes designed to work end grain, the low pitch, which requires less energy to make a cut, is desirable. There is no need for these planes to be fitted with a back iron, and this enables the cutting iron to be bedded in the plane with the bevel up.

An iron fitted into the plane with the bevel up allows the blade to be supported by the bed of the plane right to its cutting edge; this not only stops the blade chattering, but also gets rid of the gap behind the iron caused by the sharpening angle of the edge. This last feature is an asset when planing long mitres, as the point of the mitre cannot catch in the gap.

The pitch of an iron fitted with the bevel up is not the angle of the iron with the bed: the sharpening angle must be added to it. For instance, an iron sharpened at 30° would have a bed angle of 15°, to make a pitch angle of 45°. So it can be seen that single iron planes that appear to be low-angled may still be standard pitch.

THE SOLE

It is surprising how fast the sole of a gunmetal plane wears hollow, making the tool inaccurate. I always fit a steel sole to my castings, which is not as difficult as it appears (see Chapter 5). All this brings me to that most important feature: the sole that is absolutely flat, not only when the tool has just been made, but for ever and a day.

What makes a plane sole go out of true? This is one of those unanswerable questions, in that when we seem to have all the answers, another one crops up. The major reasons seem to be the following: the casting will have inherent stresses in it, and the foundry making the casting can remove these with a heat process known as stress relieving. This process is all very well, but if a steel sole is sweated

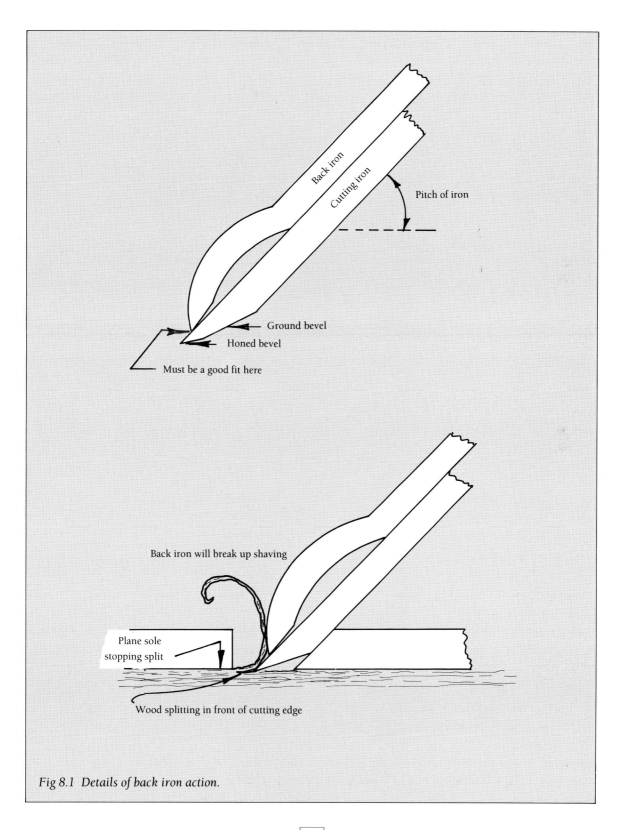

Fig 8.1 Details of back iron action.

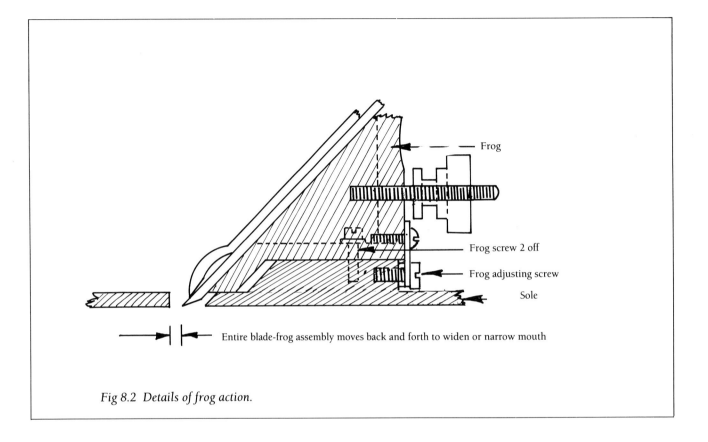

Fig 8.2 Details of frog action.

on, new stresses are introduced with the heating up and cooling of the parts. There is also the effect of different expansion coefficients between the steel sole and the bronze casting.

I may have overcome this problem by silver-soldering studs to the top side of the steel sole and bolting it to the casting through slotted holes. This means the sole can be attached without any heat being used, as the slots allow the sole to expand and contract without distorting the casting. Only time will tell if this method has worked – the first plane I made this way is now about five years old and remains flat. Of course, on small planes, such as thumb and chariot planes, this bimetal effect can be ignored.

SKIN EFFECT
Castings have a surface skin slightly different to the bulk of the metal. When the surface is worked, this skin is removed and the casting can warp, so it is good practice not to work just one surface, but to skim all those that have to be worked. Removing a similar amount of metal from each surface in a step-by-step manner, until the final dimensions are achieved, will help to preserve stability.

THE MOUTH
The width of the mouth, the gap left in front of the iron for the shaving to escape through, affects how finely the plane will work on curly-grained wood. I find the best method is to leave the mouth undersize until fitting the

iron, before opening it up with a file until there is just sufficient room for the shaving to pass through.

CUTTING ACTION

The cutting action of a plane fitted with a back iron should be fully understood, and is important in the initial tuning of a newly made plane. If it were possible to have an enlarged view at the cutting edge of the iron as it makes a cut, the following would be observed: the fibres of the wood are parting slightly in front of the actual edge of the iron, and in fact are being split apart. If the split runs further ahead of the cutting edge and the grain goes down into the wood, then the fibres are torn out. The surface of the wood is left rough, and it is said that it was planed against the grain.

The amount the fibres are allowed to part ahead of the cutting edge must be kept to a minimum if the finished surface is to be smooth. This can be achieved by three factors: first, the pitch of the iron, which has already been discussed. The second is keeping the width of mouth to a minimum. As the shaving is cut, what is actually happening is that a layer of fibres are being split off, and as the shaving runs up the front of the iron it forms a lever, making the split in front of the edge run further forward. If the mouth is narrow, the pressure of the sole in front of the mouth on the surface of the wood prevents the splitting.

The introduction of a back iron to break up the length of the shaving, thus reducing the length of its leverage effect, is the third way of controlling the cut. The shape of the back iron has some influence on how efficiently it performs this duty: it is most important that the edge of the back iron, where it mates with the cutting iron, is a perfect fit. If there is the slightest gap between the two irons, the

shaving will jam in it and further shavings will build up, until the mouth is jammed full and the plane will no longer work.

HANDLES

When it comes to designing handles, the size of your own hand should be taken into account. By picking up and using different planes and consciously noting how comfortable or otherwise the handles are, you will soon learn what suits you. Once the ideal handle has been made, and after you have used it for a time and are satisfied with it, make a template for future use.

Comfort is not the only consideration to be made about the plane's handle, for not only is the plane pushed forward but it must also be held down; this is most important when working difficult wood. As the handle at the back of the plane leans forward, a line drawn at right angles to the centre line of the handle should pitch somewhere near the mouth of the plane.

The shape of the knob at the front of the plane can be individual to you. Subtle changes in shape make the world of difference when using the plane for any length of time. I have changed all the knobs on my Bailey pattern planes to the low pattern ones fitted by Stanley before 1922, as they allow me to work over the plane much better than the high modern knob. When it comes to the cushion-shaped knob fitted to the traditional English steel plane, there is even more scope for individuality: I like a really deep groove round mine so that the tips of my fingers can get a good grip.

THE BLADE

No matter how much thought and effort we put into the making of the plane's body, the finished tool is only as good as the blade. This fact is brought home when one considers the amount of money that Japanese woodworkers are prepared to pay for a blade made by one of their top blacksmiths. What a pity it is that we are unable to buy a suitable blade made by these craftsmen for our traditional English planes. Years ago there were some fine irons to be found, made from cast steel without modern additives, but unfortunately plane irons wear out. If you are lucky and find a good old parallel iron nearly ¼in thick, you will have the main ingredient of a perfect tool. When looking at old irons, do not be put off by a bit of rust – if it has not pitted the iron too deep, this is of no account, and for a few pounds a local engineering firm will surface grind an old iron, making it flat and true and removing all surface damage. A mildly rusted iron can be put back into commission by being rubbed on a flat steel plate with carborundum paste. Motorists' and DIY shops sell this paste for grinding the valves in car engines.

Some of the very best old plane irons were laminated – the good expensive steel was laminated on to a softer steel. Inspection of the side of the iron will reveal the join line if it is not apparent on the face. Most of these old irons are superior to anything that we can buy or make today, and it is therefore worth going to a good deal of trouble to acquire them.

If we have to make our own irons, it is best to start with new steel. This is bought as gauge plate; a plate is about 6in wide by 18in long; it is in a natural state, soft enough to be cut with a hacksaw and filed. It is not a difficult task to cut and shape an iron, but it will still need heat treatment. The label on the wrapping round the gauge plate has details of the treatment that is required for various degrees of hardness. If you are making an iron for a quality plane, I suggest that the heat treatment be entrusted to a specialist firm; ask them to heat-treat it to 61° Rockwell 'C', and not to come lower than this, but to err on the high side.

THE BACK IRON

The gauge plate referred to in the last paragraph is ideal for making back irons, which do not need to be heat-treated. Of course there is no need to buy gauge plate specially for this purpose; most steels, even of unknown quality, will do. What is important is the shape of the back iron. The tip where it fits on to the cutting iron needs to be fashioned into part of a semi-circle (*see* Fig 8.1). The function of the back iron is to peel the shaving away from the cutting iron with a clean action: there must be no tendency for the shaving (no matter how thin) to crumple up against the tip of the back iron.

Special Purpose Planes in Wood

Fig 9.1 *Small curved rebate plane.*

Numerous planes are needed by the various woodworking trades; from the cooper's jointer, around 6ft long, to the pattern makers' smallest core plane, all have their special function. Many of them have always been made by the craftsperson themselves, quite often to fulfil one special task. However, there are many special purpose wooden planes that were once produced by manufacturers for the trade.

The photographs in this chapter show a range of planes I have made, which were all made to fill a particular requirement. Some are in frequent use, others may only be used once in several years, but when they are needed, it is good to have them there, ready and waiting.

IDENTIFY THE NEED

I make no excuse for repeating what has been stated in an earlier chapter: 'make sure you

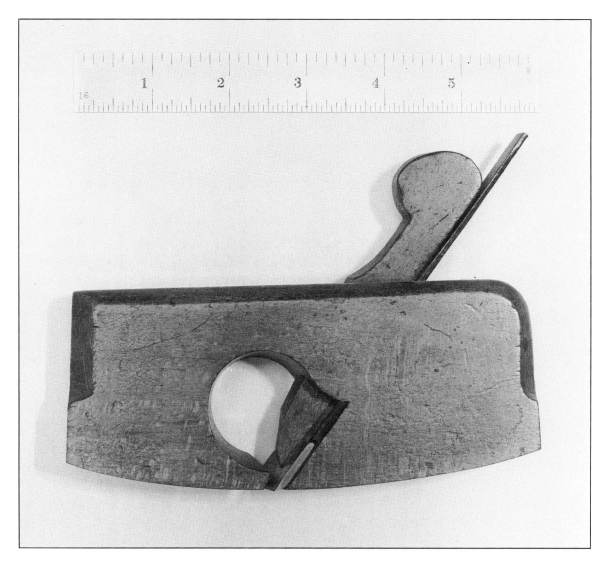

Fig 9.2 Beech compass plane with skew mouth.

know exactly what you want to achieve before starting to make the tool'. So often time has been wasted because a horse was made when really a camel was required.

There is a wide selection of small planes in the photographs; studying these may give you some help in designing your own. Each photograph has a rule included to give a guide to the size. The method of construction is very much the same for them all.

To describe the making of these special planes, it will be easiest if they are broken down into two distinct types. First, I shall describe the making of the small thumb planes. These are similar to but smaller than the moulding planes we are all familiar with. Then comes the other type of plane, where the shavings escape through the top of the plane rather than the side; this type of plane is usually referred to as mouthed.

SELECTING THE WOOD

It is pleasing to make little planes from a piece of good hardwood that is a bit too small for most other purposes, but is nevertheless a prized piece. This not only makes the construction a pleasant undertaking, but the finished tool is then a bit special (*see* Fig 9.1). Fruit wood is one of my first choices, and even some of the exotic tropical woods could be used. The planes made by manufacturers were usually made from beech or hornbeam, and many of these are still around after 100 years or so.

It is important that whatever wood is chosen is of a stable nature. Mild fine grain is needed; this means that the sole wears evenly and the tool is pleasant to handle. Splintery, coarse-grained woods are to be avoided for this reason.

The orientation of the grain is important. The annular rings should be parallel with the sole. If beech is used, the medullary rays will be at 90° to the sole; not only does this ensure stability, but the figuring on the sides of the plane can be most attractive (*see* Fig 9.2).

The Japanese use oak for the bodies of their planes; they call the body the *dai*. Such importance is put on this that the *dai* is made by a craftsman who does nothing else. While I have the utmost admiration for the Japanese toolmakers and use many tools made by them, I would not use the oak freely available in this country for a plane body. The Japanese makers have specially chosen their timber for the purpose, and it is of an entirely different nature to most of the oak I have met in this country.

METALWORK

The small blades needed for these miniature planes are easier to make or come by than those required for full-sized bench planes. I have even seen old chisels used, but would not recommend this, as they are too thick. I have a stock of old machine hacksaw blades; these are about 1½in wide and ³⁄₃₂in thick. Although this high-speed steel will not take quite as good a cutting edge as high carbon steel, it works adequately for the purpose, and the blades can easily be cut out with a grinder.

On planes with a flat sole which are to be frequently used, a piece of plate brass is often fixed to the sole. This can be secured with brass countersunk screws. If the countersinks are kept shallow, the screws can be filed down flush with the sole. In this way the screwdriver slots will be removed and the screws will not show. On some planes, such as the chamfer-plane, other parts require to be made; these are also cut from plate brass.

FIRST STEPS

Having made full-size drawings of the intended plane and obtained a suitable piece of timber, the first task is to plane the wood. The preparation follows conventional lines: first a face side is planed dead flat and straight, and the face edge is planed straight and square to the face side. If you followed the setting out procedure explained in Chapter 5, this would be a good time to put it into practice. The engineering method will be more accurate than normal woodworking practice, and this will familiarize you with it. The width and thickness of the block can be marked using the surface plate and scribing block.

The body of the plane is set out by marking out lines square round both ends of the block of wood, the length of the plane apart. The mouth is marked on the sole and a pitch line drawn from the back of the mouth to the top edge on the face. Remember that a single-ironed plane will require a steeper pitch than one with double irons. For your first plane it is best to make a square mouth; once all the procedures have been mastered, a skew mouth is an easy progression. Set out another line on the side, forward of the pitchline. This represents the wedge room. The curved opening through which the shaving escapes (*see* Fig 9.3) is next marked on the side of the block. Looking at the side of the block, there should now be lines representing the final shape of the plane. These lines are squared over the top and bottom edges so that the setting out can be transferred on to the other side of the block.

There are two methods of cutting away the wood to be removed. The easiest way is to saw the block in half – you then have two pieces of wood the shape of the plane but half its width. The wedge room can now be worked with saw chisel and router, just like making a housing joint. The two parts are then glued back together to form the finished body of the plane.

Fig 9.3 *Small beech compass rebate plane.*

However, this is the easy way out and not the method adopted by the plane makers of old. You may prefer to do the job in the conventional manner. The finished plane will not have a joint line down its length; the curved opening through which the shaving escapes is first cut out right through the block. A hole is drilled from the top of the plane in the wedge room, right through the block at the pitch angle. The drill will break through into the curved opening previously cut. Working from the top with a chisel, the hole is squared up and cut to the required shape. The accurate drilling of this hole may be a bit of a problem – if you are lucky enough to own a pillar drill, the block needs to be clamped to the table at the required angle. The drill is then fed into it slowly and carefully. If you have to manage with a brace and bit or even a hand drill, then things become more complicated. Two strips of thin wood about 1ft long are clamped one each side of the block, with one edge on the pitch line. The bit or drill must be kept between and at the same angle as these strips.

The mouth is cut next: leave it as fine as possible, opening it up later, when you fit the blade. Sight down the inside face of the hole where the blade will bed. Is it flat and straight? If not, take a sharp chisel and carefully make it so.

The blade will need to be made next; blade making is discussed in Chapters 2, 6 and 8. The blade will have to be entered through the mouth, which will now need opening up to allow this. Grinding the narrow part of the blade might be necessary, both in width and in thickness.

There is a feature here that must be mentioned: with single-ironed wooden planes, the iron is wedge-shaped in thickness. This is because, when loosening the iron, it can be

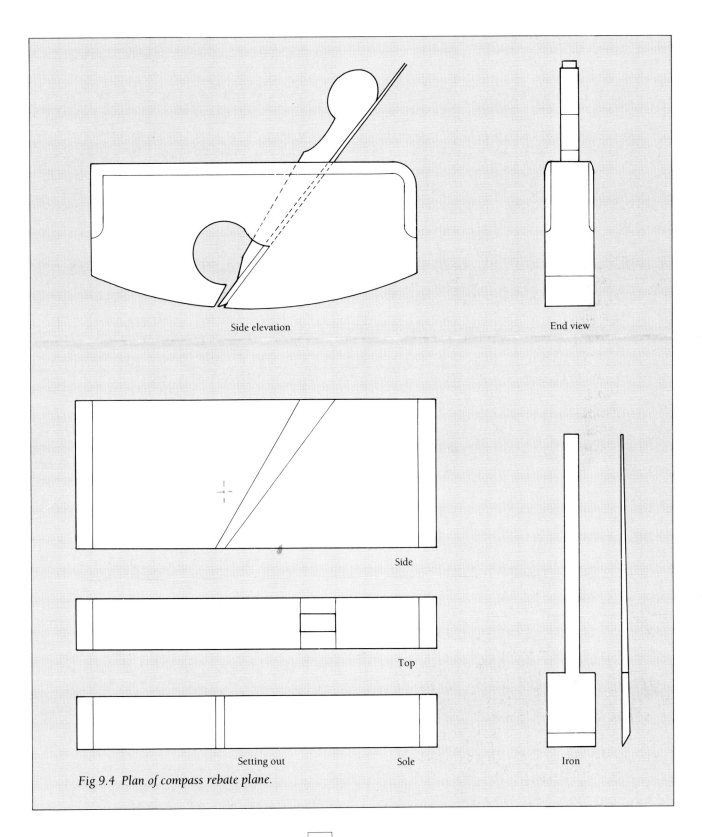

Side elevation

End view

Side

Top

Setting out   Sole

Iron

Fig 9.4 Plan of compass rebate plane.

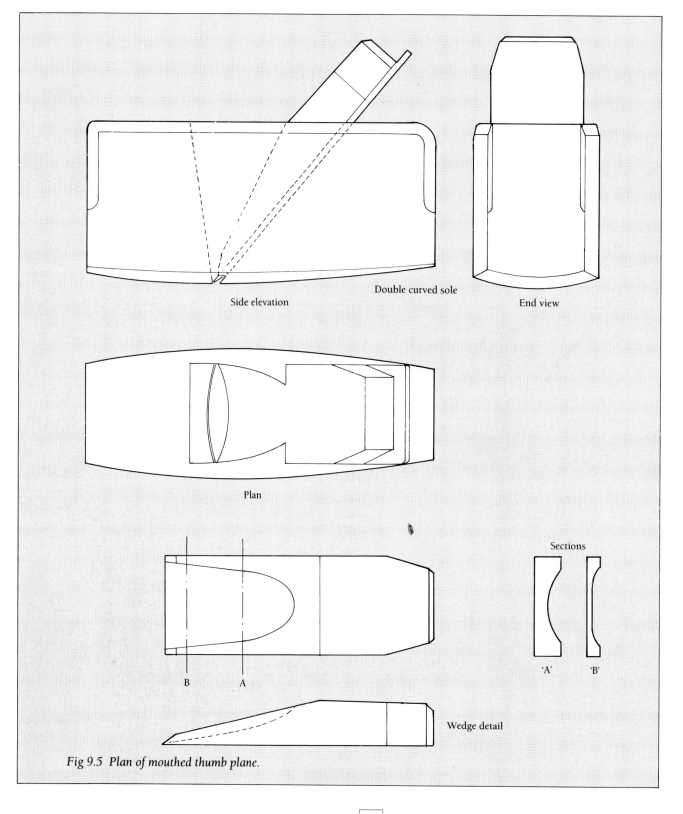

Side elevation

Double curved sole

End view

Plan

Sections

'A'   'B'

B   A

Wedge detail

Fig 9.5 Plan of mouthed thumb plane.

tapped down further into the plane. As the iron is wedge-shaped, it becomes looser the further it is driven in. The wedge can then be pulled out by gripping it between the fingers. Most secondhand planes have had their wedges ruined by people who did not know how to remove them: the top part of the wedge has been hit under the round with a hammer, and is badly disfigured.

All that remains now is to make and fit the wedge. It is best to stick to the traditional shape, which has been perfected over several hundred years and works fine. Figs 9.4 and 9.5 show two wedges, both of which are suitable for the type of plane being discussed. Planes made before 1750 had the wedge with the round top; after that time, the top gradually changed to the ellipse. If you acquire some old moulding planes that have had their irons battered, you will need to make a quantity of new ones, and there is a way of mass-producing them. Strips of wood are prepared to the correct thickness and the right size to make one wedge. The strips are clamped together side by side and the whole block worked to the required shape. A small amount of wood should be left to allow for individual fitting.

TUNING UP

The construction of the plane is now completed; if it works well straight away, you may consider yourself very lucky, as most times a certain amount of fettling will be needed. Try taking a long thin shaving from a piece of straight-grained deal. Does the shaving clear the plane properly? If not, you will need to inspect the plane carefully to find out where the shaving is fouling up. The curved opening may need slight reshaping to throw the shaving out of the side of the plane, or the shaving might be catching on the end of

the wedge. This fine-tuning can take quite a while on your first plane, but with experience the various vagaries of a plane can soon be found and put to rights.

When a skew-mouthed plane is to be made, the first step is to decide which side of the plane the shaving will escape from. The pair of circular rebate planes shown in Fig 9.6 are left- and right-handed. Pairs of planes are skewed opposite to one another: a plane made to work in a rebate needs to throw the shaving out from the side away from the edge of the rebate. Failure to observe this feature in the design will make a plane that keeps choking up with shavings that cannot escape from the mouth.

Once the plane is working to the maker's satisfaction, all that is left to do is to apply some form of finish. I soak my planes in a bath of linseed oil – this has been the traditional treatment since planes were first made. Once the wood has soaked up as much oil as it will

Fig 9.6 Curved rebate planes, right- and left-handed.

hold, it is placed on a pile of old newspapers. Quite a lot of the oil will bleed out, but this will not take long – a day in the oil and a day bleeding is all that is required. After a few months of use the oily wood takes on a fine patina: this is a good hard-wearing finish, and a plane so treated seems to stay stable even in adverse conditions.

MOUTHED PLANES

Much of what has been said about the making of the thumb plane applies equally to mouthed planes. These planes are usually much larger than those previously discussed – all bench planes in daily use are of this design. Mostly they are of the double-iron type; this method of wedging the iron makes for a chatter-free plane. Bench planes are those in everyday use on the bench, such as jack, smoother, trying, jointer and so on. While they cannot be described as special planes, they illustrate the design of the mouthed plane very well.

Fig 9.7 Miniature compass plane, with the sole rounded in both directions.

Because wooden bench planes require more skill to set up and use, they have fallen from favour; the modern tendency to de-skill most crafts has led to the adoption of the cheap, mass-produced metal plane, and the secondhand market is knee-deep in old wooden bench planes. So, unless you particularly want to make your own, good examples of the more common types can be obtained for a reasonable price. A wooden plane in good tune is a revelation to use: the wooden sole gives far less friction than a metal plane, and glides over the work in an effortless way (*see* Fig 9.7).

THE EASY WAY OUT

All the intricate cutting is done inside the mouth of these planes. It is easier by far to make them from two pieces and join them after all the shaping is carried out; however, all those that I have made have been from one solid block of wood (*see* Fig 9.8).

This style of plane comes in all sizes, from the minute to the gigantic. The core planes illustrated in Fig 9.9 are probably the smallest, but not the easiest to make. I made my own jack plane many years ago, and since then I have made several as special presents for friends. If there is much wood to be removed from a job, there is nothing like a wooden jack: shavings like soldiers' belts can be removed.

As with all woodworking projects, the first task is to prepare the timber. I find it best to set the plane out on the side of the block, as even when there is no cutting to be done on the side, the lines are there as a reference.

The accurate forming of the mouth and shaving escapement can be approached in several ways. If you have a pillar drill and some machine bits, much of the wood can be removed with them. The difficulty is that the opening has to be worked entirely from the top of the block, and this opening gets smaller as it gets deeper. Controlling the accurate cutting of these slopes and not removing too much wood is not easy. It is helpful if the bevel required is worked on a scrap piece of timber, which can be held on top of the block and the chisel worked at the angle of the scrap piece.

The fitting of the wedge is most important. The iron and wedge must bed down spot-on if the plane is to work well. A little chalk rubbed on the face of the wedge will show exactly where it fits or does not fit, and correction is then comparatively easy. A standard wooden jack plane is the most common plane in daily use; any other plane of this design can be derived from it.

Lastly I would remind you again that the newly-finished plane will take some time to get into fine tune, so do not be too disappointed if the plane you have spent some hours in making will not perform straight

Fig 9.8 Small block plane.

away. Persevere and patiently sort its problems out one at a time. It is worth it when you finally have a well-honed tool that is a pleasure to use.

Fig 9.9 Two miniature routers with brass soles – very useful on small work.

Tuning & Improving the Bailey Pattern Plane

The Bailey pattern plane as made by major tool manufacturers such as Stanley and Record is an ingenious tool. While not in the class of the English pattern planes made by Spiers and Norris, it is a willing workhorse. Because of the vast numbers that have been mass-produced it is relatively cheap to purchase, and because it is mass-produced some hand work will improve it. The amount of work that is worthwhile must be a personal decision based on the age and condition, but any work done will be repaid with interest when the tool is used.

HISTORY

Before working on your Bailey plane, it will be interesting to know something of its background and just how old it is. Planes made before the First World War tend to be of better quality than later ones.

In 1858 Leonard Bailey was granted his first patent for a metal plane; 23 years old at the time, this American was no doubt an inventive genius. In 1869 the Stanley Rule and Level Company purchased Leonard Bailey's company. Metallic planes were then practically unknown, and it was a brave move by Stanley to venture in to this market in the way that they did. I wonder if the directors of Stanley then foresaw the millions of Bailey pattern planes that would be manufactured in the following years?

FORGERIES?

Over the years many firms have made copies of the Bailey plane. There is nothing that somebody will not make a little poorer and sell cheaper. Sears' Catalogue for 1897 lists imitation Bailey planes. A lot of price engineering has been employed on the design of the planes of later years; these are nowhere near as good as the early ones.

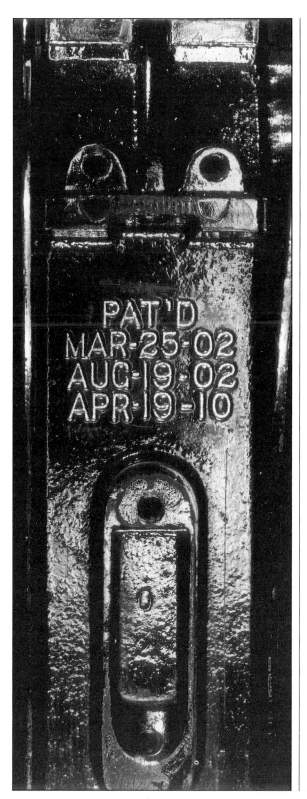

HOW OLD IS IT?

There are certain features that give a good indication of the date the plane was manufactured (*see* Fig 10.1). Probably the most noticeable feature that changes is the front knob: before 1922 this was of a lower, rounder design than the taller shape that we know today (*see* Fig 10.2). The lateral adjustment to the iron was added in 1885, and was changed in 1888 by having an anti-friction disc added to it. Some cheaper copies made today by Eastern countries revert to the original simpler design, omitting the anti-friction disc. The seating for the front knob was altered in 1936. A raised ring in the body casting surrounds the bottom of the knob from that date.

In 1933 the keyhole-shaped hole in the lever cap was changed to one of kidney shape; this new shape of hole was said to make the iron less subject to loosening during adjustment.

The solidity of the whole assembly was improved in 1905 by the introduction of a two-step frog: two raised bosses in the bottom of the new casting formed a solid seat for the frog, with longer threads for the two retaining screws (*see* Fig 10.3).

Until 1925 the lever cap was a plain casting; the name Stanley was added to it after that date. The name Bailey is cast on to the body forward of the front knob from 1905 onwards. The smaller planes (Numbers 1 and 2) do not seem to have this last feature. (As these small planes are somewhat rare, I have only seen a few and cannot vouch for this information.)

A screw to adjust the frog position was added in 1914 – this feature makes it possible

Fig 10.1 Dates on the casting of a Bailey plane body.

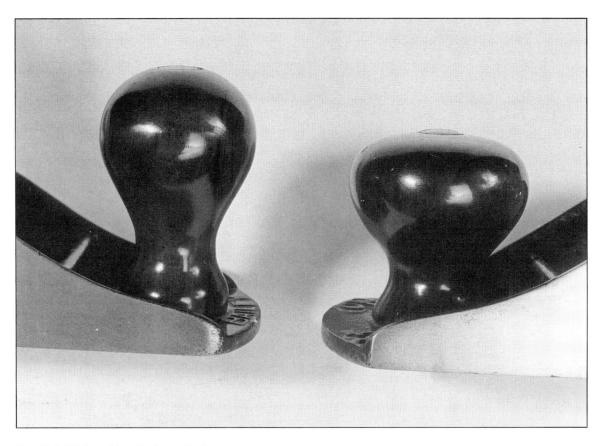

Fig 10.2 High and low knobs on Bailey pattern planes.

to adjust the size of the mouth opening accurately. All the features previously described were added before the Second World War (*see* Fig 10.4). During the war, because of restrictions on materials, the planes made in this country tended to be substandard.

Several price-cutting features have been introduced; some proved so bad that they had to be discontinued. For instance, the yoke casting that connects the adjustment wheel to the back iron, which was made for a time from two pressings of sheet metal. After a short while in use the sheet metal bent and the yoke would not engage with the adjustment wheel. The adjustment wheel was also made from steel instead of the more expensive brass.

Nearly all the planes being manufactured now have horrible plastic handles, which quite often break across the screw hole.

What might be considered an improvement is that the ribs have been added to the top side of the body casting. These are supposed to keep the casting true. I have noticed that many new planes have hollow soles when purchased: what happens is that the body castings are machined soon after casting. In the old days, the castings were left out of doors for several months to weather and settle down. Today, this would mean that money was tied up – the ribs have been added in the hope that they will counteract the stresses in the newly cast and machined body.

NEW IS NOT BETTER

From the foregoing you will have gathered that I am not very keen on the newer planes. All the Bailey pattern planes in my workshop are pre-1930. I have never thought about this before sitting to write this chapter, but they are all older than I am! Why should I be so keen on these older planes? The casting will certainly have settled down, and if it has warped it should remain true after corrections have been carried out.

The older planes with rosewood handles look far better than the horrid plastic things of today. The grinding is far superior; the surface finish on new planes is abysmal. When I complained about this, the quality assurance manager of a leading manufacturer told me that the deep scratches could be filled with paraffin wax; this, he suggested, was a good feature as the plane would then automatically lubricate itself....

THE HANDLES

Unless your plane already has the older rosewood handles, making new ones will probably be one of the first tasks. There is no point in copying the beech or plastic handles fitted to later planes, as these are crude compared with the early pattern. It is a personal preference which front knob suits you best. I like the old-fashioned low one, as I find it allows me to get over the top of the plane. The tall modern knob needs to be grasped more from the side, giving less control over the plane. If you decide to change from the tall knob to a low one, the spindle that holds the knob to the casting will need shortening and the thread on this spindle will then have to be extended; this is not always as straightforward as it seems at first sight. The thread is sometimes Whitworth: this gives no problems, but on some planes the thread is

not conventional. The easiest way out is to make a new spindle a little larger in diameter than the old one. The holes in the brass nut and the casting can then be retapped with a standard thread.

The handle, sometimes known as a tote, can be made to suit your own hand. Beech handles were routed from the flat board and a

Fig 10.3 Frogs from Bailey pattern planes. The one on the left is a modern version, that on the right is pre-1900 – note the date 1876 on the lateral adjuster.

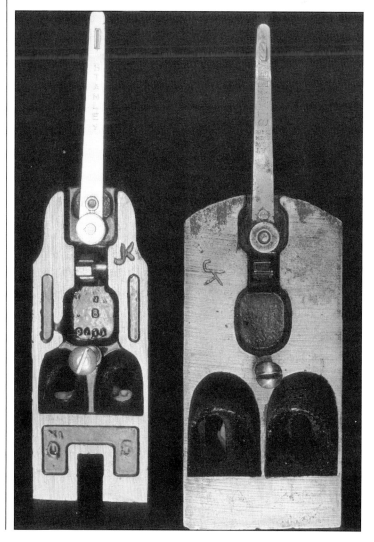

rounding-over cutter was run around the front and back profile. Where the round meets the flat side of the handle there is a nasty ridge; a real blister-raiser. Even if you do not feel up to making a new handle, a little work with a chisel and some abrasive paper will work wonders.

If you decide to make a new handle and have no pattern from which to work, modify the old one first. If you work with a sharp chisel, removing a little wood here and there, testing for comfort every now and then, you will have the basis for a well-designed handle. The section through the handle should be elliptical, and there should be no flats on the sides. Particular attention should be paid to where the top of the handle curves over between the thumb and first finger. With prolonged use, this part of the tote can rub that soft part of the hand very sore.

THE BODY CASTING

It is in the body casting that the greatest discrepancies will quite often be found. A thorough check for flatness of sole and squareness of sides should be carried out. Start by blueing up the surface plate as described in Chapter 5 (under Scraping). Rub the sole of the plane firmly on the plate and inspect the sole; all the high spots will be blued up.

A decision must now be made as to just how bad the sole is and what is needed to put it right. Take a straightedge and bridge it between blued high spots: if more than a 3-thou feeler gauge can be inserted under the straightedge, a decision must be made: what is to be done to put matters right? An engineering firm will surface-grind the sole and the sides so that all is nice and true: this is fine if money is of no object, but unfortunately most of us woodworkers are not in that happy position.

The cast body has a hard surface skin, and once through this it is fairly soft to work. This hard skin will return after a time as the surface metal reacts with the atmosphere. The metal that needs removing can either be scraped or abraded away. Some skill is needed with the engineers' scraper; the technique is described in Chapter 5.

Abrasion is much easier; the method that I adopt is as follows: a sheet of coarse aluminium oxide (100 grit) is taped down to the surface plate and the surface to be trued is rubbed back and forth on this, particular care being taken not to rock the casting but to keep it flat. When the whole surface shows signs of being rubbed all over, a finer grade of paper is used (220 grit). Inspecting the surface that is being flattened will reveal when the whole surface has been rubbed. A change of abrasive medium is now made, and successively finer sheets of silicon carbide paper are used on the surface plate. When rubbing on these last sheets, paraffin (kerosene) should be used as a lubricant. This will also prevent the abrasive from clogging up with metal dust. The final surface finish depends on how fine the grade of the last sheet of abrasive paper is. A scratch-free surface should be aimed at; this can be obtained with a 600 grit.

Having trued the sole, the sides will now need to be checked for squareness to the sole. Of course, if the plane is never used on a shooting board or similar appliance there is no need for this squareness. However, I like to know that my tools are just right, so this task is always carried out, and this is done in a very similar way to that employed on the sole. A block of metal known to be square is used. This can be another plane body or something similar – an engineers' angle plate is ideal but not essential. Fix the abrasive to the surface plate, with the square metal object that you

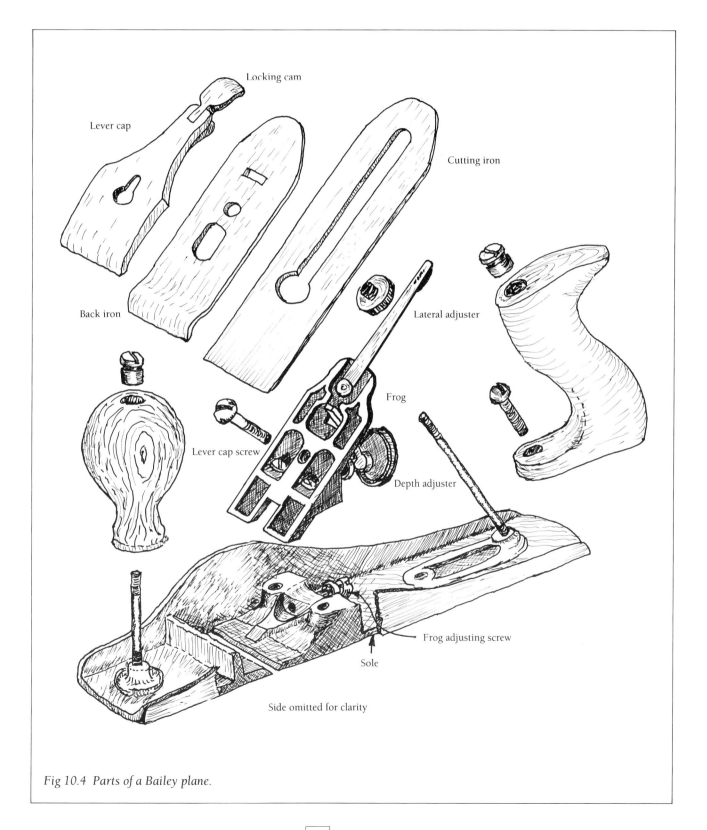

Fig 10.4 *Parts of a Bailey plane.*

Fig 10.5 Beds for frogs. Compare the much larger area of the older plane body on the left with the area of the modern plane on the right.

have for a guide along the side of the paper but not on it. The sole of the plane to be trued up is pressed hard against the square surface and rubbed back and forth, with its side on the abrasive paper. Care must be taken to keep the body being trued up firmly against the reference surface, while still applying sufficient pressure down on to the abrasive. The progress of the work should be checked from time to time, and the abrasive changed as described for trueing the sole.

When the three sides of the body casting have been trued as described above, the mouth opening should be inspected. The back edge where the iron beds will now probably have a very sharp edge; this should be removed with a file. The forward edge will probably be square to the sole – this needs modifying so that there is an easy path for the shavings to escape.

THE FROG

The frog is the next part to receive attention. The parts in the body casting where the frog beds down are coated with engineers' blue (*see* Fig 10.5). The frog and bolts holding it in place are assembled into the body casting, and the frog is then taken out and inspected on its lower surfaces to see where it has taken the blue from the body. A file and scraper are used to get a good solid fit between the two parts. At least 75% of the surface should blue up for a good fit.

THE IRONS

Whether to be satisfied with the thin iron fitted to these planes or to change it depends on what work the plane will be put to. It is not difficult to cut a new, thicker iron from gauge plate, which will perform better on difficult wood than the original iron. The thicker iron is far less prone to chatter. The making of plane irons and their heat treatment is dealt with in Chapters 6 and 8.

There have been several differently shaped back irons supplied with the Bailey plane over the years. The best performer seems to be the one with a round formed along its lower end. This is not a very difficult part to make and needs no heat treatment. It is most important that the back iron mates perfectly with the cutting iron; the slightest gap between the two where the bottom tip of the back iron beds on to the cutting iron will cause trouble. Shavings enter this small gap and jam up in the mouth, causing the plane to gag. The part of the back iron that beds on to the cutting iron is best worked flat on an oilstone in good condition. When the two irons are assembled and the screw tightened up, the assembly can be held up to the light; by looking under the round of the back iron it is possible to see just how good the fit is. No light must pass between them where the lower ends bed together.

THE LEVER CAP

As previously stated, there are two distinct designs of lever cap: the modern one with a kidney-shaped hole and the word 'Stanley' cast in, and the earlier one with the keyhole-shaped hole. The later caps were all bright nickel plated, while the early ones were left bare cast metal. The choice between the two is purely an aesthetic one. I have found no problems with the early design of cap, and in fact prefer it. Unless massive adjustments are made, there is no problem and the casting will take on a good polish with fine abrasives. Most of my planes have these early lever caps, which I have had engraved with my name (*see* Fig 10.6). This makes the plane personal, if apparently a bit ostentatious to some people.

FINE TUNING THE PLANE

With the plane fully assembled, sight along the sole and adjust the iron until it shows as a thin black line. With the plane turned upside down so that the mouth can be seen, check that the cutting edge of the iron is parallel to the front of the mouth. Before making adjustments to counteract any discrepancy, decide how wide the mouth needs to be. This width will depend on the type of work to be undertaken; for instance, a smoothing plane to be used on very fine work will need a mouth as fine as is possible to set while still clearing the shaving. A jack plane to be used to remove thick shavings will need a wider mouth. If you are not sure what you require, set the mouth with minimal clearance and adjust it wider if shavings stick in it. It will be found that most

frogs have a certain amount of play and can be slewed when the bolts are slackened off: by slewing the frog, the blade can then be set parallel with the mouth.

Fig 10.6 Personalised old pattern lever cap.

Making a Chariot Plane from Scratch

Fig 11.1 The finished chariot plane.

The plane described in this chapter is one I made some years ago. It is a Mark II version, which is to say that I had previously made one but thought it needed improving. This little plane incorporates all the improvements lacking in the first edition when in use. So far, the Mark II has performed every task asked of it to perfection, and I cannot see how it could be improved further (*see* Fig 11.1).

THE ALTERNATIVES

If this is one of the first planes you have attempted, perhaps a simplified version would be suitable, and there are several features incorporated in the design that can be omitted: for instance, the adjuster could be left out to start with and added later. The adjustable mouth and steel sole can be treated in the same way (*see* Fig 11.2).

There are three ways to make the body. A casting can be purchased – Bristol Designs produce one very similar to that illustrated here (*see* Appendix for addresses of suppliers) – a pattern can be made, and a casting commissioned from a foundry. The plane illustrated had the body milled out from a solid block of phosphor bronze, but unless the maker has a fair degree of engineering skill this alternative cannot be considered. I have seen bodies that have been made by brazing sheet material, but have never tried this myself. For the beginner and the less experienced maker, I would strongly recommend buying the casting.

If a pattern is to be made, there are a few things to add to the information in Chapter 7: the mould will be made with the sole of the plane uppermost, therefore the webs forming the sides of the plane will need to taper very slightly towards the top. The sides round over at the top and project beyond the back of the plane, which would prevent the mould being withdrawn from the sand. Fig i1.3 shows how this can be overcome by continuing the sides down the back of the plane and cutting them off after casting. A rapping plate must then be inserted in the sole of the pattern.

WORKING ON THE BODY

Start by cleaning up the casting, just removing any bumps or lumps. The amount of cleaning up depends on how cleanly the foundry have made the moulding. A good casting should need very little work before you start to bring it to the final shape required.

The sole should be filed as true as you can make it. The sides are then worked in a similar manner. I have a small surface plate on which I can continually check the progress of the work. Stand the casting on its sole on the surface plate, and then use a square to check the sides by standing the stock of the square on the surface plate. Bring the blade up to the side of the casting to check it: this is far more accurate than trying the square directly on to the casting.

Fig 11.2 The parts of the plane.

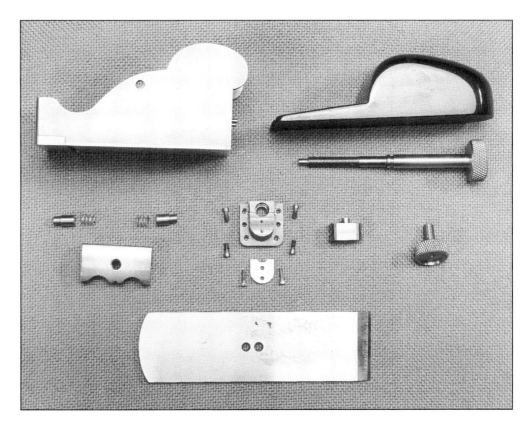

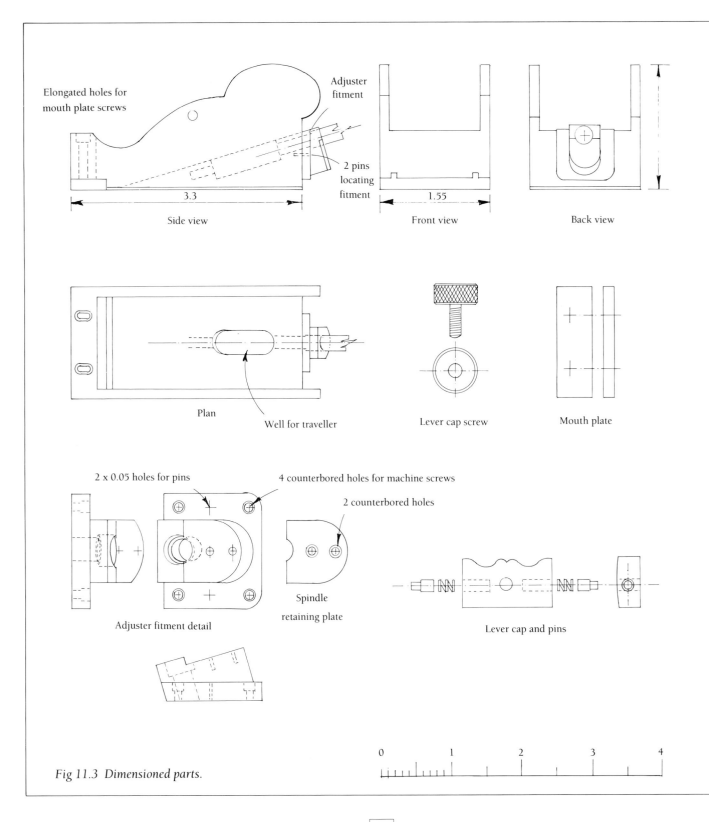

Fig 11.3 *Dimensioned parts.*

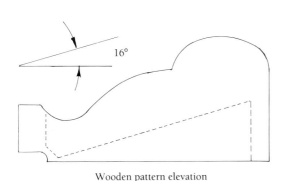

Wooden pattern elevation

16°

Wooden pattern plan view

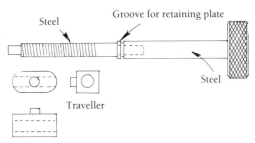

Steel

Groove for retaining plate

Steel

Traveller

Adjuster spindle – 2 parts silver soldered

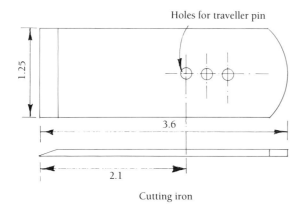

Holes for traveller pin

1.25

3.6

2.1

Cutting iron

When the sides are true to the sole, the inside of the casting must be worked on. Flat files and a square-ended scraper are best for this job. I have several pieces of metal that have a true flat face; using one of these pieces with the face blued up, it is an easy matter to locate high spots on the face where the iron beds. The part where the iron beds must be dead flat and true if the plane is to work well.

The next task is to shape the top of the sides. Over the years I have made several planes of similar construction to this one, and to start with I always had difficulty getting the shape of both sides exactly the same. This has been overcome by making a thin aluminium template of the side. the bottom straightedge and the ends; position the template on the side, and it is an easy matter to run a scriber around the shape at the top. This gives an accurate, well-defined line to work to. If the original pattern for the casting was well-made it will be a simple job to remove a small amount of metal with a file to bring the sides to their final shape.

The front and back of the body casting should next be filed square to the sole and the sides. Set out the recess for the adjustable mouth using the surface plate and a scribing block. A good deal of the metal to be removed can be sawn out with a hacksaw. The recess is finished with a flat file, using a flat piece of blued-up metal to ensure a true surface.

The holes for the adjustable mouth and the lever cap pins are marked out and drilled next. The holes for the bolts that hold the adjustable mouth will have to be counterbored for the boltheads. The holes must be elongated to facilitate the movement of the mouthpiece; this counterboring can be achieved with a twist drill, while elongation of the holes is done with a small round Swiss file.

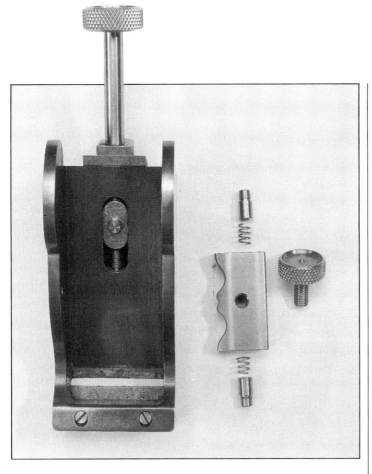

Fig 11.4 Plane stripped out to show adjuster and lever cap.

On this Mark II version of the plane, I have included a feature to keep the mouthpiece in line when it is being adjusted. There are two tiny grooves in the body which engage with tongues on the mouthpiece. This useful feature is not essential, as it is quite a difficult task to cut the parts accurately by hand. However, if you accept the challenge, it can be done by working methodically with chisels and files. (If you have access to machining facilities it is a straightforward matter to mill the parts.)

The steel sole should be the next part to receive attention. The sole on this particular plane is a piece of old worn-out rip saw blade. Cut out a piece of steel a little bigger than required – once fitted, it can easily be filed down flush with the sides of the plane. It is

very difficult to position the steel accurately when all the parts are at soldering temperature, so care must be taken. The procedure for sweating the steel sole on to the body is described in Chapter 5.

Once the sole has been fixed and trimmed flush all round, the mouthpiece should be fitted. The sole is rubbed flat on abrasive paper fixed to the surface plate. The lever cap is held in position with a riveted pin on all planes made to this pattern, including large bench planes; this means that once fitted it cannot be removed. I have always thought that this was a nuisance, as quite often when work needs to be done on a plane, the lever cap is in the way. I have overcome this problem by fitting stepped pins with a spring between them: Fig 11.3 explains this better than words can. The lever cap can then be removed by depressing both stepped pins, giving uninterrupted access to the inside of the mouth.

THE LEVER CAP

The lever cap is filed out from a solid piece of brass bar. First cut and file the block to an exact fit between the sides of the plane. The easiest way to get the top profile correct is to first drill the hole right through the cap; this hole should be the correct dimension from the lower flat face and a sliding fit for the spring. Counterbore both ends of the hole for the stepped pins and insert the spring and stepped pins into the lever cap block. The block is pushed in between the sides of the plane with the stepped pins depressed. When it is in the correct position, the pins will be pushed by the spring and snap into their respective holes in the sides. A scriber can be used to mark both ends of the block from the profile at the top of the sides. It is then an easy matter to remove the block by depressing the pins. File

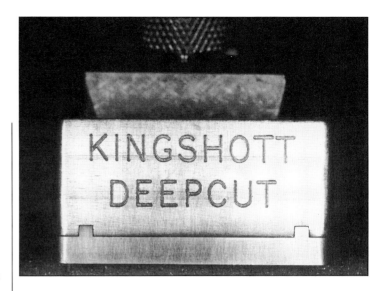

Fig 11.5 Front of the plane, showing engraving and adjustable sole.

the top to the lines scribed from the sides. The fancy shape on the lower edge of the lever cap can now be worked; this is where you can show off and make any elaborate or simple shape that takes your fancy.

To make the knurled screw that retains the wedge and iron will require the use of a lathe. If you do not have one, there are many people whose hobby is model making, and the local library will give you the address of the various model club secretaries. From there it should be a short step to finding somebody near at hand who will help, and a reciprocal job of woodwork will usually get all sorts of metal bits and bobs turned up. This is how I managed for years – the adjuster on this plane was made for me by an instrument maker in return for a small toolbox.

If the worst comes to the worst and you have to manage without a lathe, the wedge can be used to hold the iron. The screw is just a refinement, and of course it would work just as well with a screwdriver slot in the head instead of being knurled. Instructions for making and heat-treating the iron are given in Chapter 6.

THE ADJUSTER

If you have access to a lathe, or have made contact with someone who has, making the adjuster is a relatively simple job. However, without a lathe it is almost impossible. Most chariot planes made by the well-known manufacturers had no adjuster. Figs 11.3 and 11.4 show exactly how this part works; there is little need for a detailed explanation of its construction, as anybody capable of making it will have no problems interpreting the illustrations.

THE WEDGE

Quite a small block of wood is required to make the wedge, and it is worth your while obtaining a piece of suitable exotic hardwood. The wedge of my plane is made from African blackwood (*Dalbergia melanoxylon*). The top part of the wedge can be tailored to fit into the palm of your hand. One finishing touch is the brass insert that the end of the lever cap screw bears on: the wedge on the Mark I version of this plane did not have this feature and finished up quite mangled.

FINISHING TOUCHES

All metalwork on the plane should now be polished using a fine grade of waterproof silicon carbide paper. Start with 320 grit and use finer papers as the surface improves; when there are no discernible scratches from using 1200 grit, finish off with metal polish. After a few months the bronze casting will take on a fine patina (*see* Fig 11.5).

The wood should have some form of finish that will seal the surface and keep it clean. The old manufacturers used French polish, but this can soon become chipped and scratched. I have used a melamine-formaldehyde lacquer for several years now; the finish on my planes has been much admired and is as good today as when it was first applied. There are several makes of this lacquer; the one used here is Jacksonmel.

Bronze Thumb Plane from a Proprietary Casting

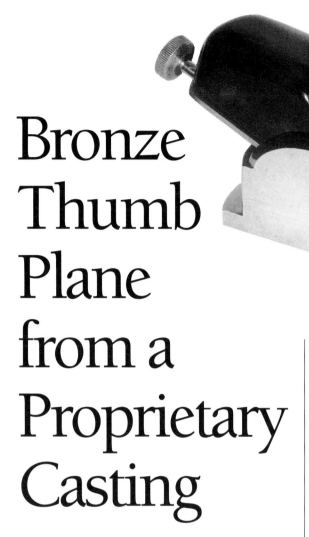

Fig 12.1 *The finished gun metal thumb plane.*

This is one of my favourite tools, and has proved so useful I would be lost without it (*see* Fig 12.1). No machine was used in its manufacture: the casting is naval gun metal obtained from Bristol Designs (*see* Appendix). This is a very good project for the would-be plane maker who lacks experience.

THE BODY

The castings supplied by Bristol Designs are of very good quality, and the work required to finish them is therefore an easy matter. On such a small plane all the work can be done with files – refer to Chapter 11 for a detailed explanation of work on the body, as the construction of this plane is very similar to the chariot plane.

Making an accurate clean mouth is about the most difficult task in producing the body. The problem is that the steel sole is difficult to position accurately when it is being sweated on. I make the steel oversize and file it down to the body size after it has been soldered; this means that the mouth has to be worked through the steel after sweating. If there was a means of positioning the sole accurately, the mouth slot could be worked first, and this would simplify the job considerably. I have not used the following method, but will try it on my next plane. You might like to try it, as it should ease the task of filing the mouth slot in the steel.

Bring the bronze casting to the state where it is ready to have the steel sole fitted. Cut the steel slightly oversize and attach it to the body with double-sided adhesive tape. Make two small metal dowels from a thick gauge of steel wire or wire nails. You will need a drill to make a hole in which the dowels are a tight fit – if you do not have a drill of the correct size, choose one a little smaller and turn the dowels down to fit with a file and the electric drill. It is surprising how much turning can be accomplished in this way. The drill **must** be secured firmly; it is not difficult to make up some form of fixture to accomplish this.

The part to be turned is placed in the chuck and brought to shape with a file. Keep the file on the move, or the teeth will soon clog up – there is also less likelihood of the part ending up with an uneven surface if the file is kept moving. Two holes are now drilled through the steel into the casting, one forward of the mouth and one behind it. Remove the sole from the body and clean the adhesive tape from the parts. The two dowels are now cleaned up and pushed into the holes in the casting.

Ease the holes in the steel sole so that it will slide over the dowels and into position on the casting. Do not make the holes too large: the steel should be held firmly in position but still be easy to remove. The mouth can be worked by drilling and filing the steel when it is detached from the casting. Although some cleaning up will be required after the sole is finally soldered on to the casting, most of the cutting can be carried out first. The dowels will of course need filing down flush with the sole; they will not show on the finished plane.

THE LEVER CAP

A casting from which to make the lever cap was supplied with the body, but I did not use this as it seemed a bit on the small side. A short piece of brass bar was used – unfortunately the brass is a slightly different colour to the bronze casting.

When working metal I follow very similar procedures to those when working wood, so the first job is to file the brass square and flat. The ends are worked true and to an overall length that just fits between the sides of the plane. Before any shaping is done, it is best to drill the holes for the pin and the tapping hole for the thumb screw. The screw was salvaged from an old mahogany camera, but required rethreading. The hole in the brass is tapped before filing the block to its final shape.

I fixed the lever cap into position with a brass pin. The holes should be countersunk in the body; the ends of the pin can then be riveted to stop it falling out in use. This riveting should be left until all other work is complete, as the lever cap will otherwise be in the way when fitting the adjuster and making sure the iron beds properly.

THE ADJUSTER

When I made this adjuster the only power machinery I had capable of cutting metal was an electric drill. Fig 12.2 shows all the parts, and I will describe the making of each one as I did it at the time.

The spindle is made from a 6in wire nail, cut slightly longer than required. The end was turned down to size by spinning the part in the electric drill and cutting the metal with a file. The knob on the end of the spindle was part of an electric terminal. The spindle was threaded to receive the knob, which once in position was centre-popped to stop it screwing off in use.

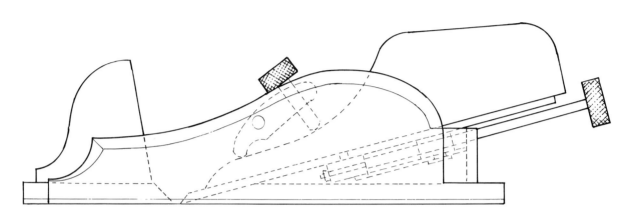

Assembled plane

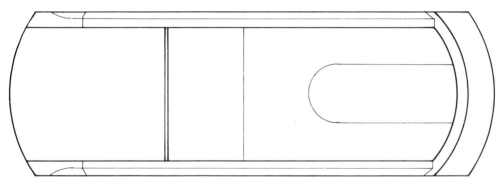

Casting and wood infill plan

Fig 12.2 Parts and details.

The traveller is made from an off-cut of mild steel bar – the pin is silver-soldered into it first. The hole through which the spindle passes was drilled next, and the end of the spindle turned down to fit it. These parts should be a good working fit, with no sloppiness. The end of the spindle is threaded to receive the nut that holds the traveller on; this nut is fixed with Loctite in the final assembly to prevent it from undoing when the plane is adjusted.

The swivel is made from a short length of ½in diameter brass bar. The hole for the spindle was drilled and tapped in a bar about

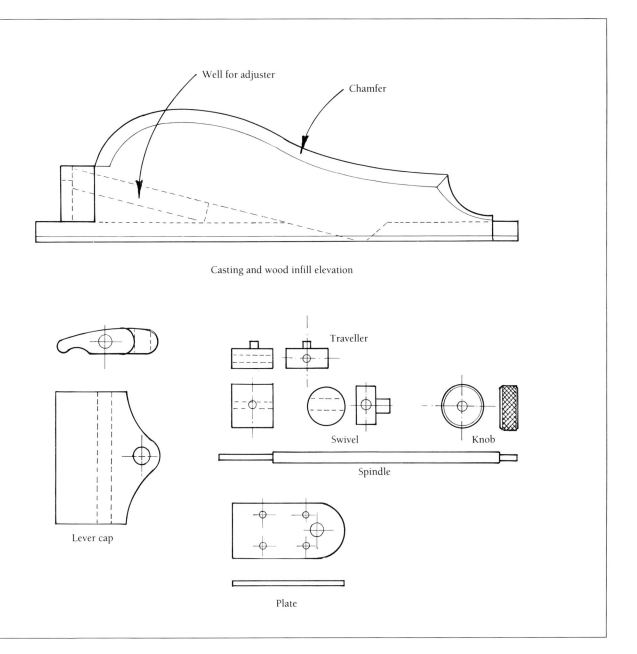

Well for adjuster

Chamfer

Casting and wood infill elevation

Lever cap

Traveller

Swivel

Knob

Spindle

Plate

2in long. The bar was put in the drill chuck and the end turned down with a file. The part was then cut off to length and the top was filed true.

The plate is cut from a sheet of 16G brass sheet, and is a straightforward job of sawing, filing and drilling. With all the parts made, assemble the swivel through the plate and washer, then peen the end over with a hammer. This part of the operation needs to be handled with care: support the top of the swivel on a heavy block of metal, so that the hammer blows will have the greatest effect. Do not use heavy blows but numerous light ones.

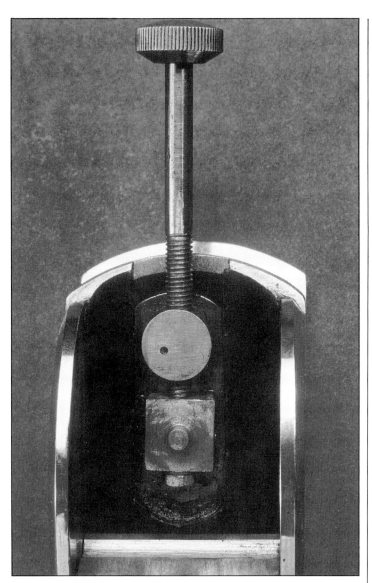

Fig 12.3 *Top view of adjuster, with wedge and iron removed.*

WOOD INFILL

The infill should be made from a piece of stable hardwood. As the adjuster is to be mounted on it, any movement will upset the precision of the tool, so the denser the wood the better. The old plane makers used rosewood (*Dalbergia nigra*). As only a small piece is needed, it is worth going to some lengths to obtain matching bits for the three parts, the front infill, back infill and wedge.

The back infill has the adjuster mounted on it. The job of cutting the housing for the adjuster is best carried out before the infill is finally fixed into position with Araldite. The back end of the body casting may need some filing so that the adjuster spindle has sufficient clearance when used for lateral adjustment (*see* Fig 12.4).

The front infill is worked to shape and fixed with Araldite; this is a straightforward job and should not present any problems. The wedge length should be made to fit the user's hand – the comfortable use of the plane is dependent upon this, so it is worth spending time getting it right. The best method is to make the wedge a bit on the long side and then reduce it until it feels comfortable. The little brass insert in the wedge makes a nice finishing touch: it is cut from 20G brass sheet and bent to the contour of the wedge. This part can also be fixed in place with Araldite.

THE IRON

The iron in this plane is a modified block plane iron. A new iron for a Stanley No.60 block plane was purchased, and a piece of mild steel shaped to be an interference fit in the cut-out was made (*see* Fig 12.5). This

Put the knob on to the end of the spindle and centre-pop it with a sharp centre punch. Screw the spindle through the swivel and attach the traveller with the nut and washer. Check the adjuster for smooth operation and fit of components: there should be no play up and down on the traveller, but the knob should turn easily. If all is well, the nut holding the traveller can be removed and then replaced, with Loctite in the threads (*see* Fig 12.3).

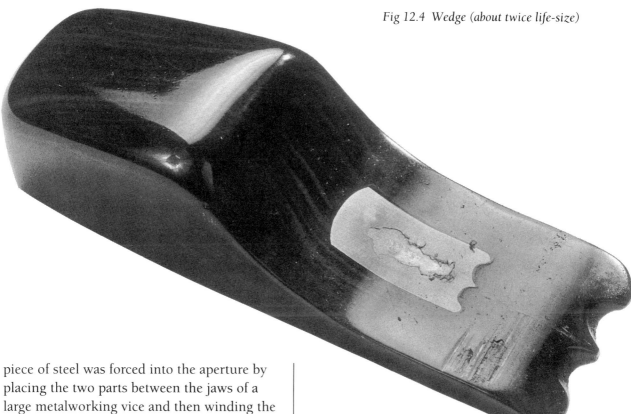

Fig 12.4 Wedge (about twice life-size)

piece of steel was forced into the aperture by placing the two parts between the jaws of a large metalworking vice and then winding the jaws closed. To make this procedure easier, the edges of the insert were filed slightly out of square; this makes it easier to align the parts prior to pressing in the vice. The holes in the iron receiving the pin on the traveller are drilled and made a good fit, as any slackness affects the precision of the adjuster.

IN CONCLUSION

Finishing and tuning have been dealt with elsewhere in this book. They are somewhat of a personal thing, as it is the personalizing of the tools that makes their manufacture so worthwhile. If you have worked through this and the preceding chapters, you should now have a good concept of the principles for making a plane from a casting.

Fig 12.5 The finished iron on the left; standard Record iron on the right.

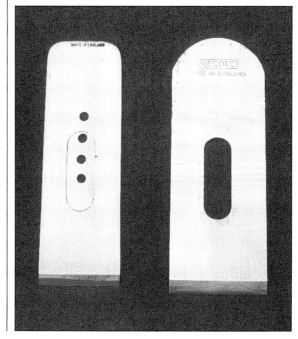

British Dovetailed Steel Plane

Fig 13.1 Original Stewart Spiers panel plane. The Norris pattern adjuster has been fitted at a later date.

BACKGROUND

The development of this sort of plane owes much to the Scottish cabinetmaker Stewart Spiers. Stewart was one of six brothers, all apprenticed to the family cabinetmaking business in Ayr. While on a visit to Edinburgh in 1840, he saw a rough iron casting for a plane, which he purchased for 1/6d (7½p). He returned to Ayr with his purchase, which he finished and sold for 18/6d (92½p). This encouraged him to give up cabinetmaking and turn to plane making – his planes were exhibited at the Great Exhibition of 1851, and he also exported many planes to America (see Fig 13.1).

Several engineering firms copied Spiers planes; some were of comparable quality, some not. The best-known of these firms was

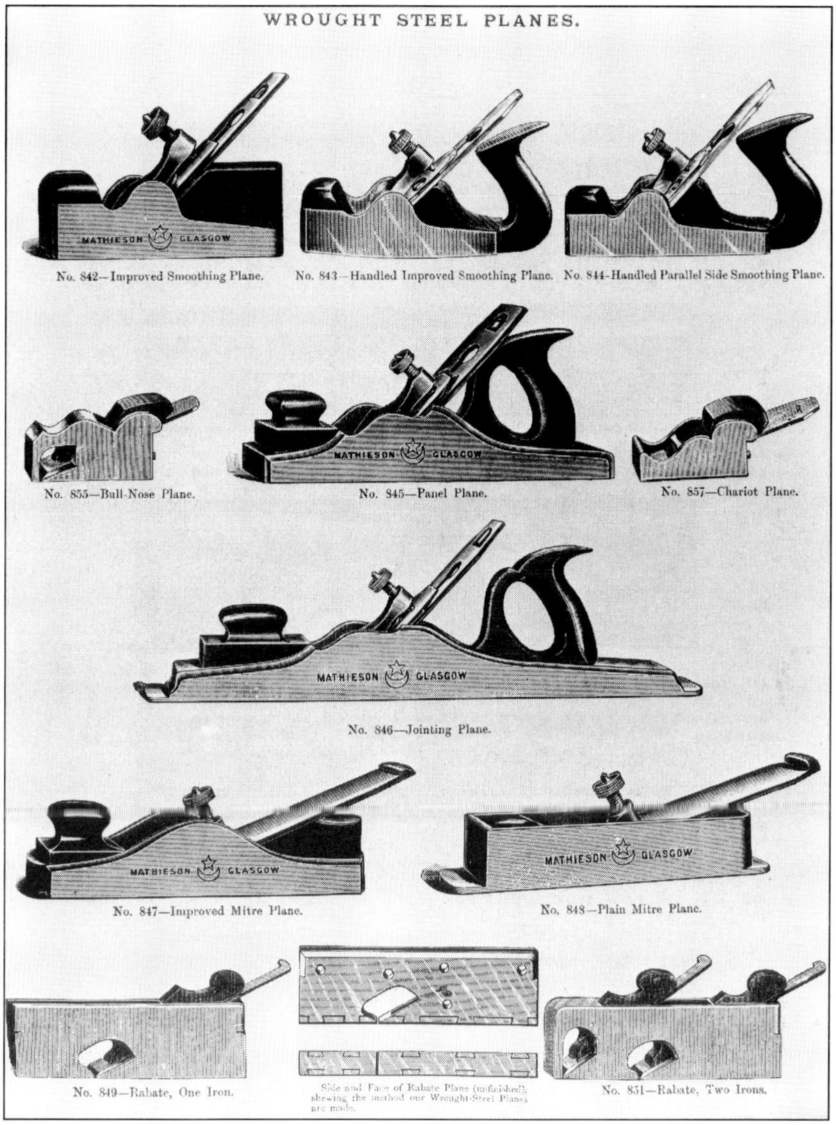
WROUGHT STEEL PLANES.
MATHIESON GLASGOW
No. 842—Improved Smoothing Plane.
No. 843—Handled Improved Smoothing Plane.
No. 844-Handled Parallel Side Smoothing Plane.
No. 855—Bull-Nose Plane.
MATHIESON GLASGOW
No. 845—Panel Plane.
No. 857—Chariot Plane.
MATHIESON GLASGOW
No. 846—Jointing Plane.
MATHIESON GLASGOW
No. 847—Improved Mitre Plane.
MATHIESON GLASGOW
No. 848—Plain Mitre Plane.
No. 849—Rabate, One Iron.
Side and Face of Rabate Plane (unfinished), shewing the method our Wrought-Steel Planes are made.
No. 851—Rabate, Two Irons.

Fig 13.2 Page from Alex. Mathieson & Sons Ltd's catalogue of 1899.

Thomas Norris of London. An introduction to the 1909 Spiers catalogue makes mention of 'numerous imitations' (*see* Fig 13.2).

At least six generations of cabinetmakers owe a debt of gratitude to Mr Spiers. The concept of dovetailing steel plates together had been previously used to manufacture a few high-class mitre planes, but it was Spiers who applied it to bench planes. This superior method of plane making is very labour-intensive, and one can understand why these planes command such high prices.

Because all the plane's body is made from plate material free of the latent stress inherent in a casting, the plane stays very true. It is also possible to work to much closer tolerances with this method of construction.

The larger bench planes were made in lengths of 13½in to 17½in, and are known as panel planes. The planes of 20½in to 29½in are called joining planes; the making of these bench planes, from the 13½in up to the longest, is described here. Fig 13.3 shows a 14½in panel plane, and templates are given for longer planes, up to a 20½in jointer. A 7½in smoothing plane is described in Chapter 14. The making of the longer planes follows very similar lines to that described for the 14½in.

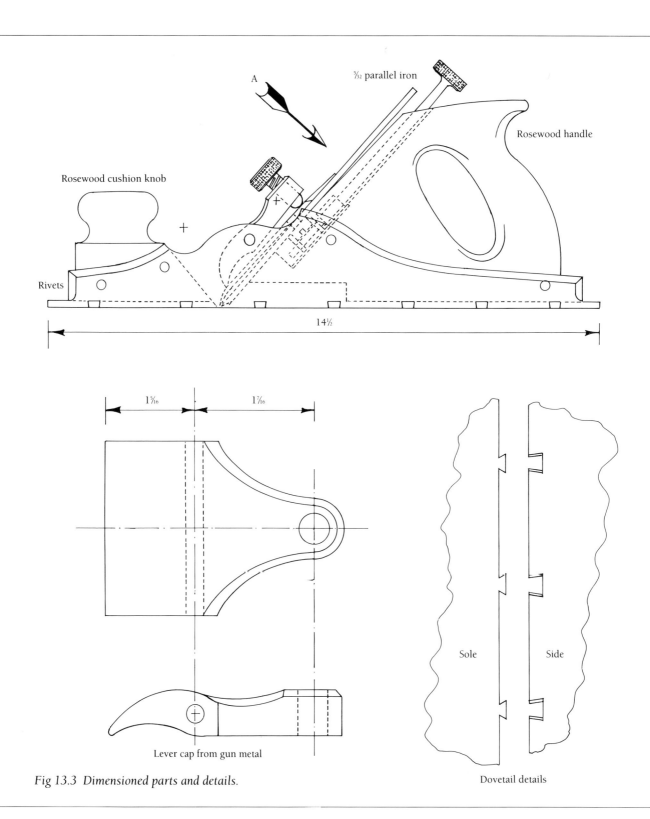

A

³⁄₃₂ parallel iron

Rosewood handle

Rosewood cushion knob

Rivets

14½

1³⁄₁₆   1⁷⁄₁₆

Lever cap from gun metal

Sole   Side

Dovetail details

Fig 13.3 Dimensioned parts and details.

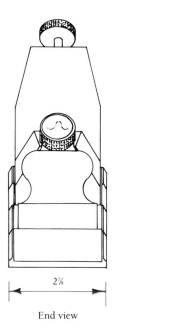

2⅞

End view

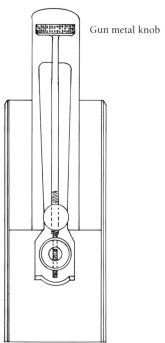

Gun metal knob

View on A with lever cap and irons removed

MATERIALS

Several years ago I purchased a very battered body of a Norris 20½in jointer; I think it had been used as an anvil (*see* Fig 13.4). I had to strip out all the hardwood infill to straighten the sides. Stamped into the inside of the sole were the following words: 'Malleable Steel, Made Especially For Thms Norris'. Exactly how this steel varies from the bright mild steel that is freely available today I do not know, but mild steel has worked very well in the planes I have made. The soles on all of the planes, with the exception of my 30in jointer, are ³⁄₁₆in thick. The sides I have been able to measure on various Norris planes seem to vary in thickness: I make mine from ⁵⁄₃₂in thick plate, but ⅛in will do, particularly if you are trying to keep the weight down.

THE TEMPLATE

The tables overleaf show stations measured from the front of the sole in inches. The tables give the height of the top profile of the side measured up the station line from the base line. The way to set out the shape of the side is as follows: draw a line that represents the sole in side view, and at the left-hand end draw a perpendicular line that will represent the front end of the sole. Measure the stations along the sole from this line; put a tick for each station. Now draw perpendicular lines at each tick, and plot the height up each of these station lines from the table.

In several places the top profile is formed by part of a circle; the diameter is given in the table. With French curves or a spline, connect the points to give a profile of the side. A thin aluminium template of the side should be made, taking care that the curves at the top are fair; if they are not, correct them. When you are satisfied with the shape of the template, drill a hole in it and hang it up until required, as it is bad practice to leave templates lying about amongst the swarf on the bench.

HOW TO USE TABLES FOR DRAWING THE SIDES OF PLANES

Station is a measurement along the sole from the front end.

Line is the height up the station at 90° to the sole.

Centre is the height up the station at 90° to the sole and is the centre point of a circle. Part of the circumference of this circle is the profile of the plane's side.

Diameter is the size of the circle referred to in 'centre' above.

All measurements are in inches.

SPIERS 15.5 PANEL PLANE

Station	Line	Centre	Diameter
01.50		0.50	0.80
01.00	0.32		
02.00	0.91		
03.00	1.00		
03.87	1.38		
04.07		1.80	1.00
05.00	2.20		
05.45		1.70	1.40
06.00	2.28		
07.00	2.00		
08.00	1.75		
09.00	1.54		
10.00	1.35		
11.00	1.20		
12.00	1.09		
13.00	1.00		
13.95		0.60	0.70
14.75		0.60	0.85

NORRIS 17.5 PANEL PLANE

Station	Line	Centre	Diameter
01.10		0.28	0.1.10
01.15		1.08	0.47
02.00	1.35		
03.00	1.60		
03.75	1.95		
04.20		2.26	1.10
05.00	2.15		
05.50	2.25		
06.00	2.23		
06.67		2.75	1.20
07.23	2.45		
08.00	2.33		
09.00	2.05		
10.00	1.60		
11.00	1.45		
16.30	Straight line	0.20	1.25
16.55		1.12	1.12
17.23		1.05	1.20

NORRIS 20.5 JOINTER

Station	Line	Centre	Diameter
00.7		0.95	1.40
01.12		0.23	0.32
01.60		0.73	0.45
02.00	1.00		
03.00	1.05		
04.00	1.18		
05.00	1.40		
05.72	1.72		
06.12		2.10	1.10
07.00	2.13		
07.50		1.59	1.40
08.00	2.25		
08.55		2.89	1.40
09.16	2.55		
10.00	2.4		
11.00	1.9		
12.00	1.55		
13.00	1.32		
14.00	1.20		
15.00	1.12		
16.00	1.05		
17.00	1.00		
18.00	0.95		
19.00	0.90		
19.00		0.67	0.45
19.90		0.90	01.4

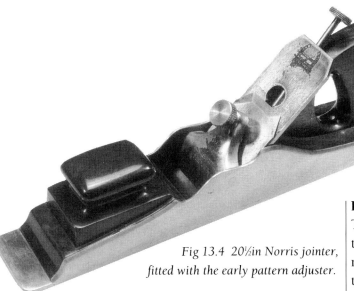

Fig 13.4 20½in Norris jointer, fitted with the early pattern adjuster.

THE SIDES

Take the two pieces of steel for the sides and coat the face of one of them with setting out blue. Use the template to scribe the shape on to the blued surface (*see* Chapter 5), marking the centres of the rivets that go through the body. Cramp the two pieces of metal together, lining up their edges. Drill ⅛in holes on the marks where the rivets will be. These holes are now given a slight countersink and the two plates are riveted together – soft aluminium rivets are ideal for this task, being easy to work, and as they are only temporary they can easily be removed. The two sides are now worked as one piece of metal.

There are several ways to cut out the profile of the sides. If you have a bandsaw that will take a metalcutting blade and run at the correct speed, you are ideally equipped. Probably the next easiest method is to use a jigsaw equipped with the correct blade. An Abra file in a hacksaw frame can be used if no form of mechanisation is available. If the work has to be done entirely by hand, I find the easiest way is to use a small drill: holes touching one another are drilled right round the part to be cut out. Whichever method you use, the steel sides will need to have the profile cleaned up with a file, to the line that was scribed on to the blued surface.

DOVETAILS IN STEEL

The dovetails that hold the sole and the sides together are considerably different from those made in wood. The first big difference is that they are splayed in both directions: this of course is impossible in wood, but steel, being malleable, can be peened to fit the second splay. The angles of the tails are also different to those used in woodworking (*see* Fig 13.5). When setting out the dovetails, make sure that one is not adjacent to the plane's mouth – the slot for the mouth extends to the full width of the internal size of the plane, and the sole will be cut into two if there is a dovetail in line with the mouth.

When using this method of joining two flat plates of steel together for the first time, it is best to have a practice run on some scrap. It is not all that difficult, but making the joint

Fig 13.5 Double splay dovetails in steel.

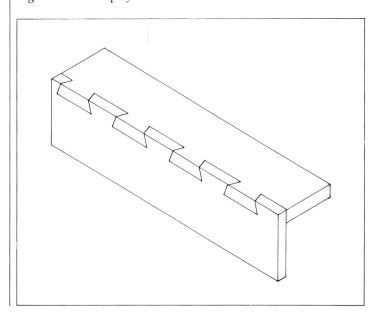

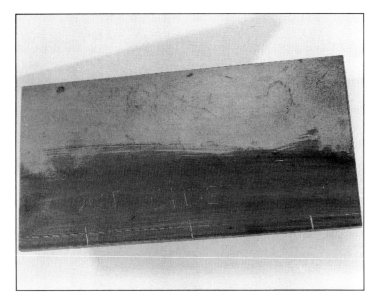

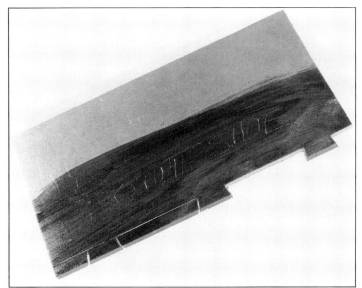

Fig 13.6 (top) Edge coated with setting out blue and with dovetails marked out.

Fig 13.7(a) (middle) Dovetails partly cut out.

Fig 13.7(b) (bottom) Dovetails cut out ready to be cleaned up with fine file.

once will indicate just how the various techniques are employed; the second attempt will be such an improvement on the first that time spent practising will be more than repaid.

Because the tails on the sides are splayed both ways when completed by peening, only the bevel in edge view is cut prior to assembly. Spare metal will be needed to form the second bevel, so the tails are slightly longer than the thickness of the sole. The process of forming this joint is difficult to explain in words, so step-by-step illustrations are included (*see* Figs 13.6, 13.7, 13.8 and 13.9). If the joint is made properly, it is almost impossible to detect on the finished plane.

THE SOLE

The steel plate for the sole is marked out on its blued-up surface and filed to shape. I allow extra width so that there is some metal to file away after assembly; $\frac{1}{64}$in on each side is plenty. The sockets for the dovetails can then be marked out and filed to the finished shape. A very fine slot can be worked where the mouth will be – the final shaping of the mouth should be left until the iron is fitted into the partly finished body. There is a piece of $\frac{3}{8}$in thick steel riveted to the sole behind the mouth; this piece gives the back of the blade a firm support and stops chatter. I use five $\frac{1}{8}$in countersunk rivets to attach this piece to the sole. Leave the attachment of this block until the sides have been assembled on to the sole.

Fig 13.8(a) (top) Dovetails assembled on to edge of mating part with sides of tails scribed.

Fig 13.8(b) (middle) Holes drilled in parts to be removed.

Fig 13.9(a) (bottom) Assembled parts ready for peening.

Be very careful when riveting through the sole, as it is very easy to deform the metal; care should be taken at all times to keep the plates flat. Any damage done to the parts can be cleaned up when the parts are all together, but quite a lot of metal may have to be removed to rectify even a small fault, and this is very time-consuming and best avoided.

ASSEMBLY

A block of hardwood – beech is ideal – around which the plane can be assembled is prepared. The width should be a perfect fit between the sides of the plane, and the length a few inches longer than the sole. The depth is not critical as long as it is greater than that of the sides.

The temporary rivets that hold the sides together are drilled out and any burr around the holes removed. Cramp one of the sides in position on the block of wood – the tails should protrude above the surface of the wood, and the flat between the tails should be exactly flush with the wood's surface.

When you are satisfied that the side is in exactly the right position, secure it with screws through the rivet holes. The sole is now placed in position and held in place with a cramp at each end. The previously positioned tails on the side should mate with the sockets in the sole; some fitting with a file may be necessary. The second side is then put into position and screwed to the block.

The whole assembly is held between the jaws of the vice, with suitable packing to

Fig 13.9(b) Parts peened and cleaned up with a file.

prevent the sides being marked. These packing pieces should be made level with the face of the sole to prevent the sides from bending during peening. Start with the vice in the centre of the assembled parts, with the sole uppermost: make sure the vice is done up really tight, as any movement of the parts during peening will be difficult to correct later.

Peen the end of the dovetail into its socket with a medium hammer: many small light blows are more controllable than several heavy ones. Keep the blows on the end of the tail so that it spreads out to fill the socket without bending. When the part that is held between the vice jaws has been completed, move the block and work out towards the ends. Take your time and inspect the work at frequent intervals, making sure all is going according to plan. Each tail should be finished satisfactorily before moving on to the next.

Take out the screws holding the sides to the block, leaving the cramps on to hold the assembled body in place, and open the rivet holes up with a ³⁄₁₆in drill. If you have a pillar drill, it is best to work from one side and go right through; if working with an electric drill or by hand, work from each side, trying to keep square to the side plates. These holes, with the exception of the lever cap pin holes, all need countersinking.

The spare metal around the dovetails can now be filed off; this is best done before removing the assembly from the block of wood. The ³⁄₈in thick block that fits behind the mouth is fitted next and riveted into place. There will be a tendency for the sides to pull in at the top, making the fitting of this block difficult. As spacers will be required later, these can be made now and used to spread the sides: these spacers are lengths of tube with a

³⁄₁₆in bore and should be a good fit on the ³⁄₁₆in rod that will later be used as rivets.

The spacers are made the exact length of the distance between the sides of the plane. The ends should be filed square and deburred. Fit one spacer between each pair of holes, except those for the lever cap pins.

THE INFILL

Much of the beauty of the finished plane is dependent on the choice of wood for the infill and handle. It is surprising how big a block is needed; the back infill can be jointed on its centre line if necessary. The rear infill should be fitted first: plane the block to the correct width to fit snugly between the sides. The bottom must be exactly square to the sides, but do not try to shape the top of the block at this stage. Work a splayed end on the block to suit the pitch of the iron.

Relieve the bottom of the block to fit over the ³⁄₈in piece of steel behind the mouth. Place the block in its exact position and drill through the rivet holes with a ³⁄₁₆in drill. Take the block out and open up the holes just drilled to accept the spacer tubes. Do not make oversize holes, as the holes should be a good fit on the tubes.

Fit the tubes into the holes and replace the block into the plane body. Push lengths of ³⁄₁₆in mild steel rod through the rivet holes – these lengths of rod can later be used as rivets, but for the time being they are just to keep the block in its proper position. As the block will need to be removed several times, it is best to use rods that are overlength. This will leave sufficient length protruding from the side to grasp when pulling the rod from the hole.

The cutting iron will be needed next. File the back of the mouth and the end of the ³⁄₈in plate to the correct angle, using the front of the infill block as a guide, and file the front of

the mouth using the iron as a guide. Keep the clearance as fine as possible: because the mouth gets wider as it passes through the sole, any metal removed later in trueing the sole will increase its width, so the final work on the mouth should be left until the plane is being fine tuned after all other work is completed.

Make sure that the iron is bedding down flat, and in particular that it is well supported behind the cutting end. Take a pencil and draw a line on the infill to work to round the top of the metal sides. The infill is cut to this line and finished smooth. Mark out the mortice into which the rear handle will fit; before cutting, remember to first remove any spacer tubes that pass through the mortice.

Chapter 15 describes how to make adjusters. If you intend fitting an adjuster, it is best to cut the housing for this before the block is riveted into place. Before the adjuster housing can be cut, the rear handle must be made and fitted in to the infill – most of the adjuster housing is in the front end of the handle. There is also the clearance channel up the front of the handle to clear the adjuster spindle for lateral adjustment. All these parts are worked and fitted together before riveting.

Make the front infill with its cushion knob next. This is a straightforward woodworking task; follow the same technique as that used to fit the rear infill. A refinement can now be added: when I stripped the infill from the Norris plane previously mentioned, I found two small pieces of brass soldered to the sides. I have never found mention of these in any book, nor have I seen them on another plane. The purpose is obvious when their position is explained.

The iron is slightly narrower in width than the inside dimension of the plane; this is to allow lateral adjustment of the iron. But if the lateral adjustment is to be effective, only the top of the iron must be allowed to move from side to side when adjusted. The two pieces of brass reduce the inside dimension of the plane across the mouth to exactly that of the iron's width, thus stopping it from moving.

The brass pieces are very small, about ¼in square, with the corners rounded off. They are soft-soldered into place. The top edge is rounded and faired into the side to stop the top edge of the brass fouling the iron when it is inserted into the plane.

RIVETING

The first few times I attempted this task, I made a mess of it. The rod used to form the rivet must be spread into the countersunk hole on both sides: it must not only fill the countersink, but must also hold the sides tight against the spacer. The rivet cannot be formed hot, as the heat expands the steel and the rod will not enter the spacer. I have used the following method successfully.

About ¹⁄₁₆in is needed at each end of the rod to form the rivet head; the rod is therefore cut in length to the overall width of the body plus ⅛in. A scrap piece of steel plate ¹⁄₁₆in thick and about 2in square has a ¼in hole drilled near its centre.

The plane body is placed on to a solid piece of metal, an anvil or something similar, and the rod to be riveted is pushed through the assembly. The scrap steel with the hole drilled in it is put between the body and the anvil. The lower end of the rod is located in the ¼in hole, allowing the rod to protrude ¹⁄₁₆in from the lower side of the plane, with ¹⁄₁₆in projecting above the top side.

The rod projecting above the uppermost side is spread out into the countersink with a medium-sized ball-peen hammer. When this has been done, turn the body over, remove the

Fig 13.10 *Brass lever cap with my own design of pinning – this makes the lever cap removable.*

scrap piece of steel, and form the rivet head on the other end of the rod. All the rivets are treated in a similar manner. A flat file is used to dress the rivet ends down flat with the sides of the plane.

CHAMFERING

The chamfer that runs round the top of the sides is worked with files. The dimensions of the chamfer are not equal; it extends further down the face of the sides than across their edges. Mark out the chamfer lines on the edge and side in the following way: clean the metal and coat it with setting out blue. Scribe a line where the chamfer meets the flat surfaces with a pair of hermaphrodite callipers (sometimes called odd-legs or jennys).

Using a round file, work the stop chamfer where the sole meets the sides at each end.

The rest of the chamfer is worked with flat and half-round files. The sharp arrises on the edges of the sides at the mouth opening are removed, and a soft round formed.

FINISHING THE BODY

If care has been taken in the making of the body as described above, it should be very nearly true, but it will still need some form of finishing to bring the surface of the plates from which it is made to a true flat surface. The method of achieving this is described in Chapter 10 – although the description given there is for working on a casting, the steel body is treated in exactly the same way.

The file marks left when working the chamfer will need polishing out. This is best achieved with emery sticks, which can be purchased but are easy to make. Take a length of softwood about 12in long, 1in wide and ¼in thick, and glue emery paper or wet and dry to both its flat sides. An assortment of different grades of abrasive paper should be used. The chamfer can now be polished using progressively finer grades, until a perfect finish is obtained. The paper must be stuck to a flat support – if unmounted (held in the hand) paper is used, the corners of the chamfer are softened and it becomes a round, spoiling the appearance of the finished plane.

Hold the plane in the position in which you will use it. Any modifications to the handle or knob to make it comfortable should be made now. The wooden parts need to be given a final going-over with fine garnet paper, to make sure all the small blemishes are removed. The adjuster is screwed into position and the cutting and back irons, screwed together, are tried on the adjuster. The operation of the adjuster is tested to make sure that all functions are carried out correctly. Any adjustments are best done at this stage.

THE LEVER CAP

The lever cap was traditionally made from gunmetal, but as this is not easily obtainable, I mostly use brass. The shape is clearly shown in Fig 13.3, and I have included a photograph of one of my lever caps to show how the corners are softened around the screw (*see* Fig 13.10).

There are several features on my lever cap that I would like to bring to your attention, as you may wish to incorporate them in your own design. The cap is held in place with spring-loaded stepped pins instead of a rivet, enabling the cap to be removed from the body at any time without having to drill out a rivet and then replace it (*see* Fig 13.11).

The screw has a square thread, copied from the early planes of Spiers and Norris. The square-cut knurling is also copied, as is the shape of the screw head. This makes a very elegant lever cap screw, far better looking to my eyes than one made using modern

Fig 13.11 Details of stepped pins and spring.

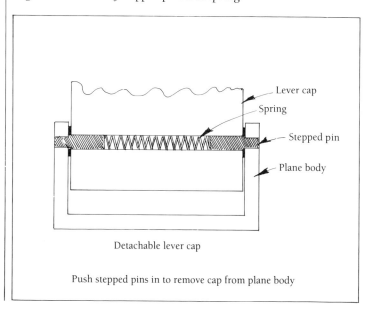

Lever cap

Spring

Stepped pin

Plane body

Detachable lever cap

Push stepped pins in to remove cap from plane body

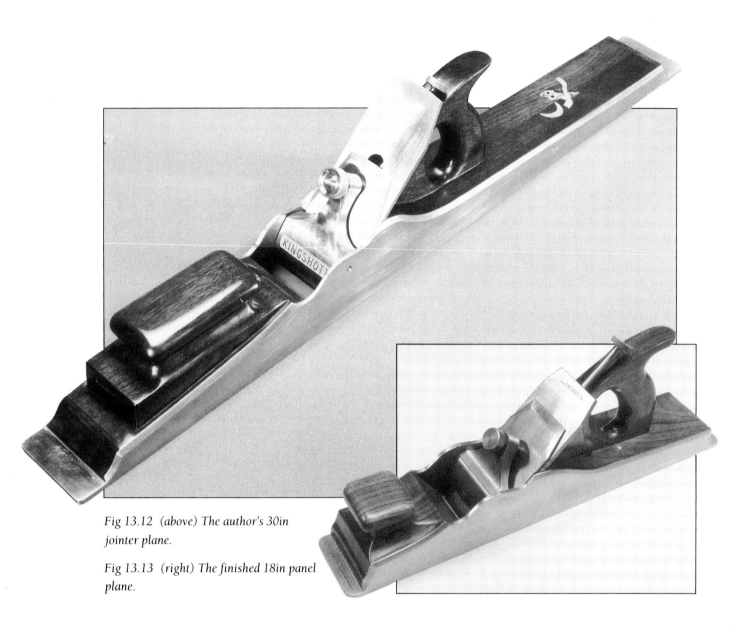

Fig 13.12 (above) The author's 30in jointer plane.

Fig 13.13 (right) The finished 18in panel plane.

techniques. Last of all, the name has been spark-eroded into the cap. This is a costly process, which I was lucky to get done on the cheap: the firm had installed a new machine, and the suppliers used my lever cap to prove the machine. However, this is the cap from my 30in jointer, for which I have turned down offers of over £3000 (*see* Fig 13.12). Having taken so many hours to make it, it would be a shame to spoil the ship for a halfpennyworth of tar, so at least have your name engraved on the cap (*see* Fig 13.13).

FINISHING TOUCHES

The wooden parts of the plane need some form of protective finish. Traditionally, French polish was used, and for these big planes seems as good as anything else. This is also a finish that can be stripped and redone if you are not satisfied with the results. Some craftsmen leave the wood bare and treat it to an occasional wipe-over with linseed oil. Over the years the oil and the constant handling build up a patina that is impossible to achieve any other way.

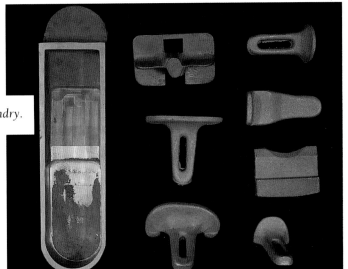

Raw bronze castings as delivered by the foundry.

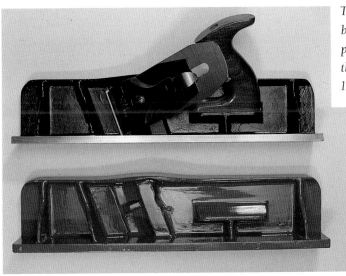

The Stanley shooting board plane and the pattern used to mould the casting (see page 121).

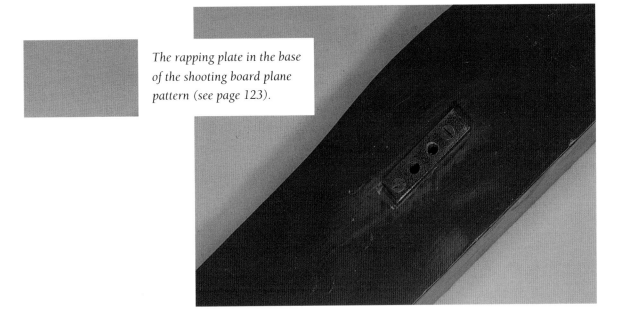

The rapping plate in the base of the shooting board plane pattern (see page 123).

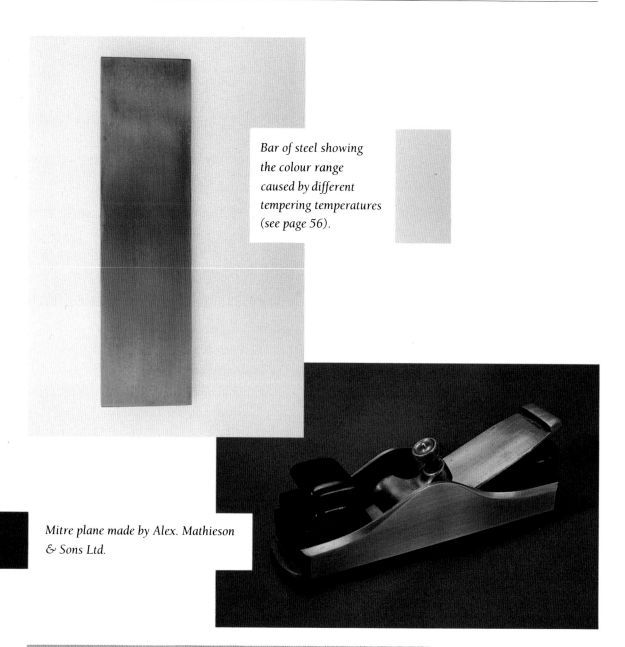

Bar of steel showing the colour range caused by different tempering temperatures (see page 56).

Mitre plane made by Alex. Mathieson & Sons Ltd.

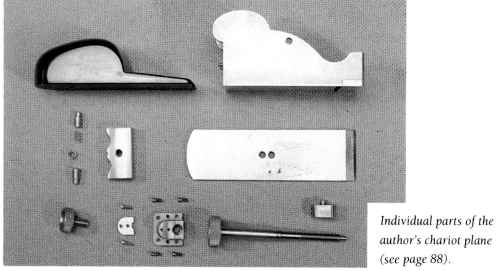

Individual parts of the author's chariot plane (see page 88).

*Original
Stewart Spiers
panel plane.*

Thomas Norris 20½in jointer.

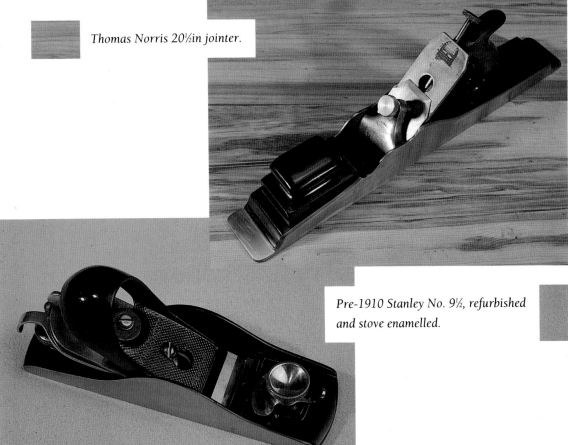

*Pre-1910 Stanley No. 9½, refurbished
and stove enamelled.*

Pair of Stanley side rebates, refurbished and bright nickel plated.

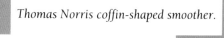

Thomas Norris coffin-shaped smoother.

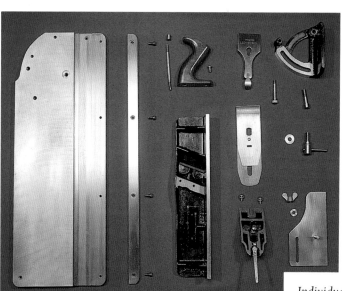

Individual parts of the shooting plane (see page 121).

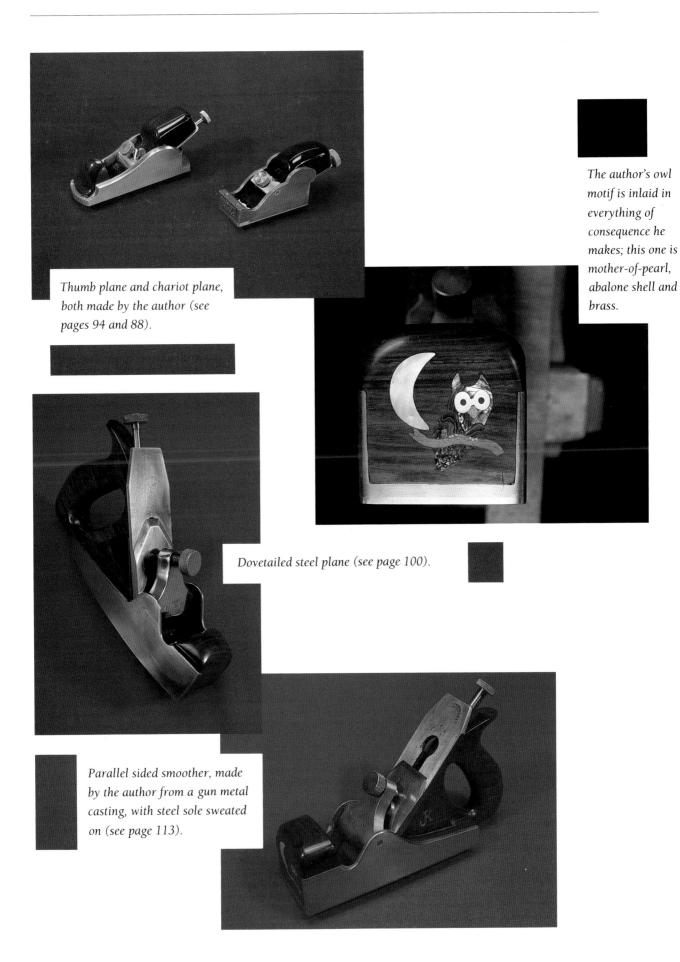

Thumb plane and chariot plane, both made by the author (see pages 94 and 88).

The author's owl motif is inlaid in everything of consequence he makes; this one is mother-of-pearl, abalone shell and brass.

Dovetailed steel plane (see page 100).

Parallel sided smoother, made by the author from a gun metal casting, with steel sole sweated on (see page 113).

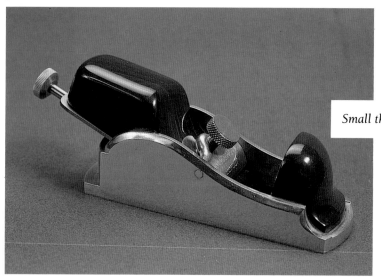

Small thumb plane made by the author.

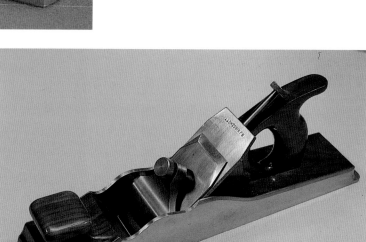

Small mitre plane, made as a present for the author's grandson.

18in panel plane made by the author.

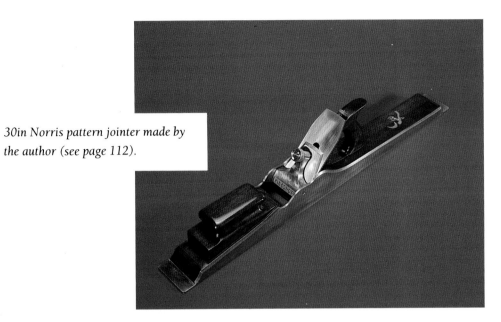

30in Norris pattern jointer made by the author (see page 112).

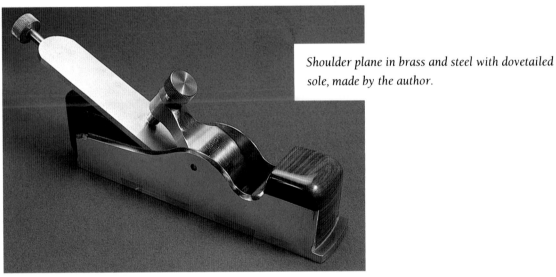

Shoulder plane in brass and steel with dovetailed sole, made by the author.

Mitre plane made by the author (see page 127).

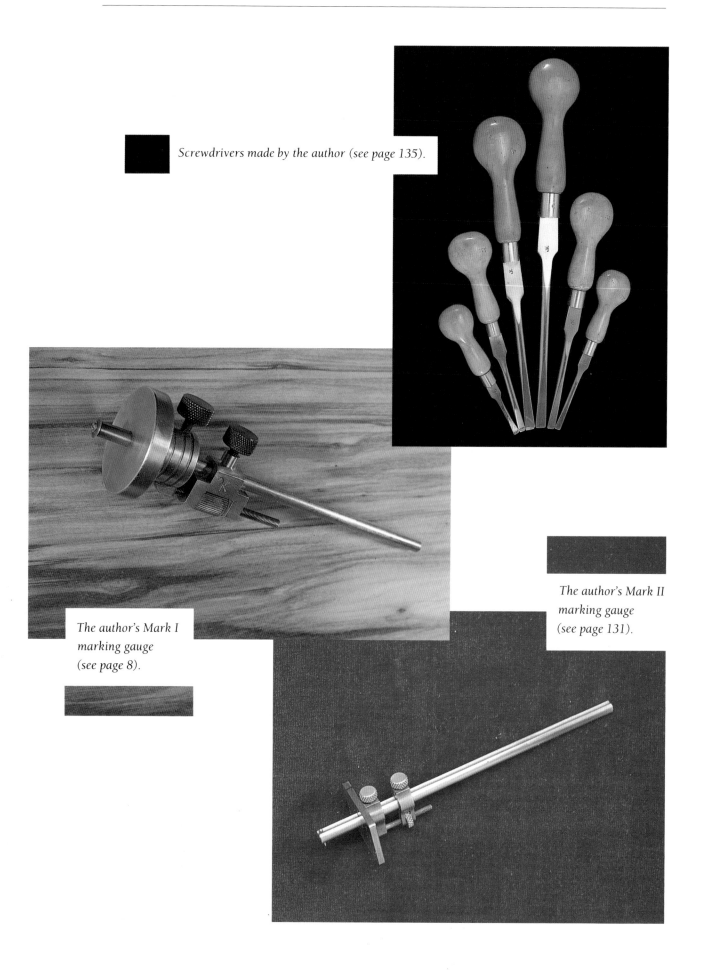

Screwdrivers made by the author (see page 135).

The author's Mark I
marking gauge
(see page 8).

The author's Mark II
marking gauge
(see page 131).

Norris Pattern Smoother

Fig 14.1 The finished plane.

This chapter can be considered as an addendum to Chapter 13, and the two should be used in conjunction. The making of the smoother follows very similar procedures to those described for the parallel-sided planes (*see* Fig 14.1). As can be seen from Fig 14.2, the main difference from the 14½in plane, other than the length, is the coffin shape, which means the sides will have to be bent. It is most important that this bending is carried out with care, or the sides may kink.

A SHAPED FORMER

A beech former the exact shape of the inside of the plane is required, and should be about 2in longer than the plane's body. Fig 14.2

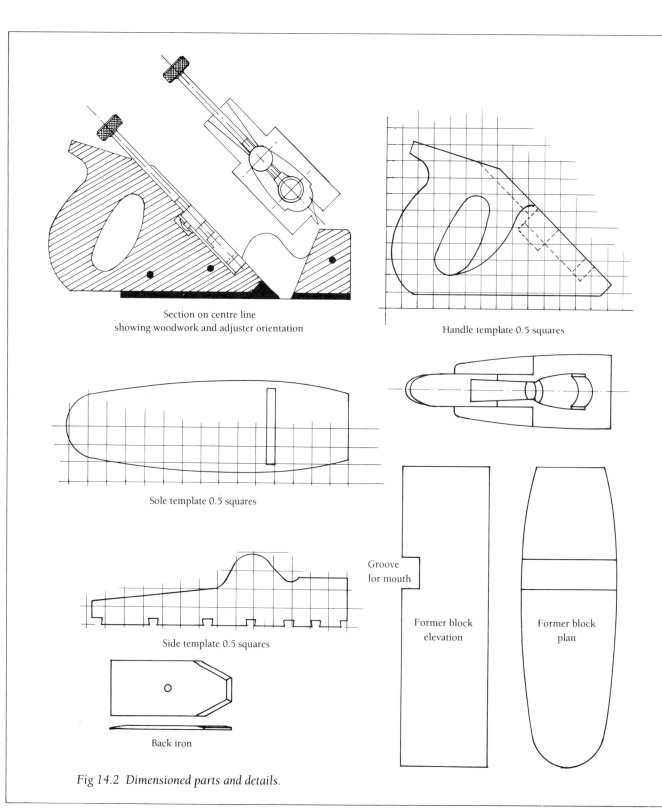

Section on centre line
showing woodwork and adjuster orientation

Handle template 0.5 squares

Sole template 0.5 squares

Groove
for mouth

Former block
elevation

Former block
plan

Side template 0.5 squares

Back iron

Fig 14.2 Dimensioned parts and details.

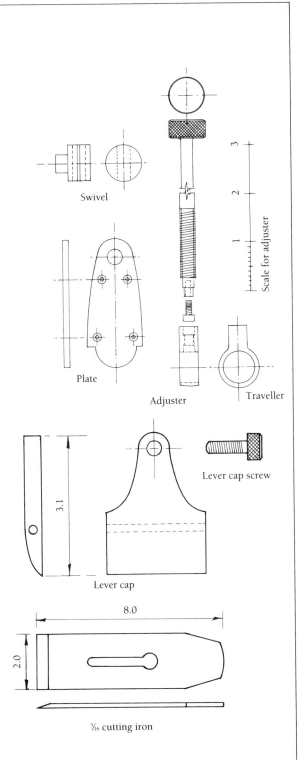

Swivel

Scale for adjuster

Plate

Adjuster

Traveller

Lever cap screw

3.1

Lever cap

8.0

2.0

5⁄16 cutting iron

shows this block, and you will notice that the dovetail positions are marked across its lower side. These are best made while the block is still square, before working the curves on the sides. After shaping, cut lines are made up the side of the block where the ends of the plane's sides locate. A line marked fore and aft on the bottom of the block before shaping will give these positions.

If you have a bandsaw, cut the sides off the block to form the shape, and save the offcuts. These will come in very useful when filing the dovetails: when they are placed either side of the plane they will make up a square assembly for cramping in the vice. If you are able to follow this procedure, it is best to allow a fairly substantial amount of timber either side of the block to form a thick offcut.

THE SOLE

The steel for the sole is given a coat of setting out blue, and the beech block is cramped on to it. Scribe a line on to the sole down both sides of the block. Take a small offcut of the steel that the sides are to be made from, and using this offcut as a gauge, scribe along both sides of the block. Mark the points where the ends of the sides locate from the block.

The front of the sole can be scribed by joining up the marks where the front of the sides end. The back of the sole is a different matter – I find that any shape to be made is best originated from a template. It is a much simpler task to file a thin piece of aluminium to shape than the thick steel sole. Therefore make a template, and when you have got the shape correct and to your liking, transfer it on to the sole.

The sole can now be cut out and filed to shape. Leave the line in when filing; it will leave a small amount of metal for cleaning up after assembly. The inside line that was scribed

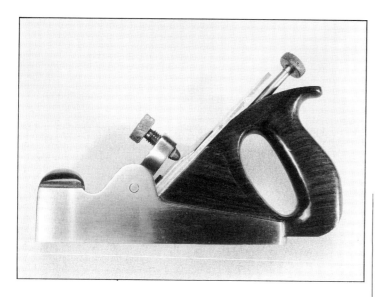

Fig 14.3 Side view of the finished plane.

directly from the block is, of course, the dovetail line. The dovetail sockets can be marked from the beech block and then filed to shape.

THE SIDES

The steel for the sides is best bent before it is cut to shape. If the steel is a parallel strip, it will bend evenly. If it is shaped, it will bend first across its narrowest point, and kink. The steel for the sides should be 2in longer than required, as this extra length will be found very useful when bending the sides. Tooling holes can be drilled in the waste to position the sides on to the beech block and to fix them there.

The sides are fixed to the block in their correct position, but with the lower edge flush with the underside of the block. The position of the dovetails can now be transferred to the sides. A pair of odd-legs are used to mark a line around the bottom of the sides; this should be the thickness of the sole plus ¹⁄₁₆in up from the lower edge. The additional ¹⁄₁₆in is an allowance for peening.

I file the dovetails in each side separately, **not** with the sides riveted together as in a parallel-sided plane, though I think it could be done that way if the dovetails were cut before bending the sides. The side being worked on is clamped to the beech block and held in the vice for this operation.

When the dovetails have been finished, the template for the side is used and the sides cut to shape.

ASSEMBLY

The procedure for assembling the body follows the same technique as that for the parallel-sided plane. The difference comes when fitting the spacers: because the ends of these have to fit against the inside shape of the sides, they are not square.

The way to get these bevels correct is to use the beech block. First locate the assembled sides and sole on to the block. Drill through the rivet holes in the sides, being very careful to make sure that the drilled hole lines up with the hole in either side. Remove the assembly from the block, and open up the hole to the diameter of the spacer, which is then placed in the hole and the ends filed to the contour of the block's surface.

Spacers made this way should be a perfect fit; however, it is important that they are orientated correctly into the infill before riveting. The riveting is carried out in the same fashion as that described for parallel-sided planes. An extra pair of hands to hold the assembly when the ends of the rivets are peened over will be found helpful. The coffin shape of the plane body makes it difficult to bed firmly on the anvil; it must be held in exactly the right position, which is difficult, but not impossible, single-handed.

The work required to finish the tool is the same as the process described in Chapter 13 (*see* Fig 14.3).

Norris Blade Adjuster

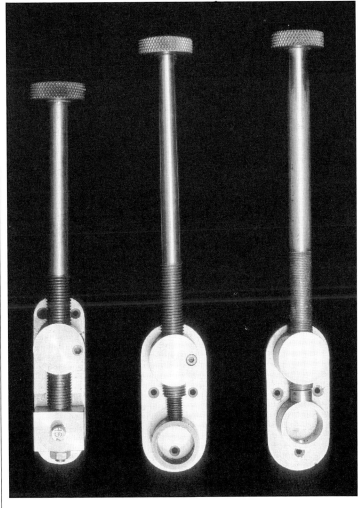

Fig 15.1 *Plane blade adjusters based on the original designs by Thomas Norris. Left to right: for a single iron mitre plane, 1923 pattern, 40 TPI micrometer thread.*

THE SEVERAL PATTERNS

In 1913 Norris patented a unique pattern of plane iron adjuster. This was a single adjustment mechanism that could regulate both the blade projection, i.e. depth of cut, and the lateral position of the blade. In 1923 a modified version was patented, with a further modification in the 1930s. Over the years I have had the opportunity of inspecting quite a

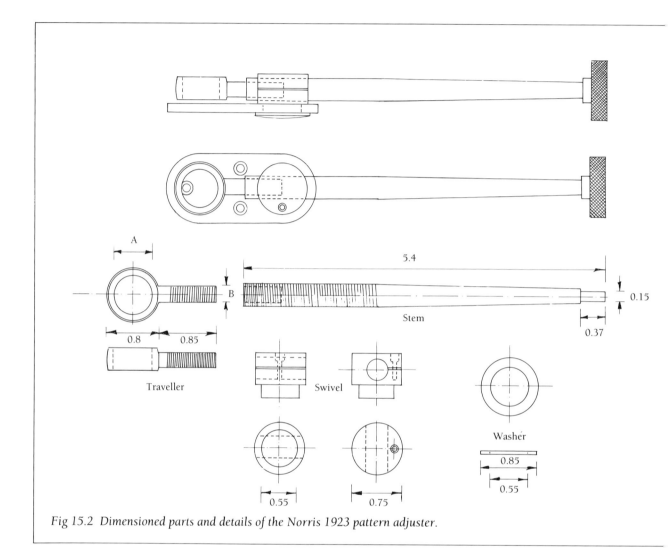

Fig 15.2 Dimensioned parts and details of the Norris 1923 pattern adjuster.

few of these Norris adjusters: all had a certain amount of play in their mechanism, which of course makes adjustment uncertain.

There are several moving parts, all of which need some clearance to operate freely. It is therefore impossible to eliminate backlash completely from the original Norris design. When making one of these adjusters it is most important to work very precisely, ensuring that all mating parts are a perfect fit. Fig 15.2 is of the 1923 pattern, though the measurements seem to have varied from time

to time. Fig 15.1 shows adjusters I have made similar to that drawn.

THE MARK III VERSION

Having made a copy of the Mark III version and used it for some time, I saw that it could be improved: there was a good deal of backlash, and the adjustments were not positive. Added to this the two threads, one right-hand and the other left-hand, gave very rapid adjustment, and I thought that if the coarse adjustment could be modified so that it

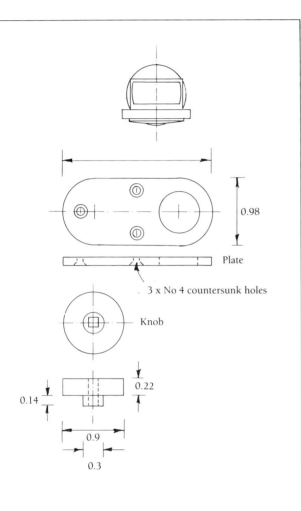

0.98

Plate

3 x No 4 countersunk holes

Knob

0.22

0.14

0.9

0.3

As backlash seemed to be introduced by the working clearance in the threads, one set was done away with and the traveller was now fixed directly to the end of the stem by a rotating joint. The stem still passed through the adjustable swivel, which could be tightened up until nearly all play in the thread was eliminated.

Now with only one thread, which in my first Mark III was Whitworth, there was still some backlash, and I still thought the adjustment too coarse. A tap and die set used to repair micrometers was acquired; the thread cut was 40 TPI (threads per inch). Using these tools, I have made several adjusters that work perfectly.

Referring to Chapter 3 on micrometers, you will see that one complete turn of the adjuster advances the blade 0.025in. Therefore, if the knob is turned 1/25 of a turn the blade will advance or retract 1/1000in – now *that's* precision!

DESIGNING YOUR ADJUSTER

In Chapter 12 there is a description of how I managed to make an adjuster without a lathe, but nearly all that I have made required a lathe. Because of my interest in modifying and making tools, several years ago I acquired a Myford ML7 lathe. It was secondhand and well used, but good enough for my purpose. Until I had the lathe I was completely dependent on a local model maker – this was fine, but meant that I had to supply working drawings of the finished item and there was no chance of changing parts on an experimental basis, for obvious reasons.

Looking at the various photographs in this chapter, you will see that adjusters based on the original Norris design can be made to fill the needs of different planes. From the chariot to the 30in jointer, all my planes are fitted

required more turns on the adjuster to move the iron, then all would be well.

An adjuster was designed and made with two right-hand threads of differing pitch, as I had previously experienced problems cutting the left-hand thread. As one thread advanced the iron the other retracted it, the difference in the pitch of the threads being the amount that the iron was moved. No matter how carefully the threads were cut, there was still far too much backlash, and so a good deal of thought was given to designing the Mark III version.

Fig 15.3 *Single iron mitre plane blade adjuster.*

Fig 15.4 *Norris 1923 pattern plane blade adjuster.*

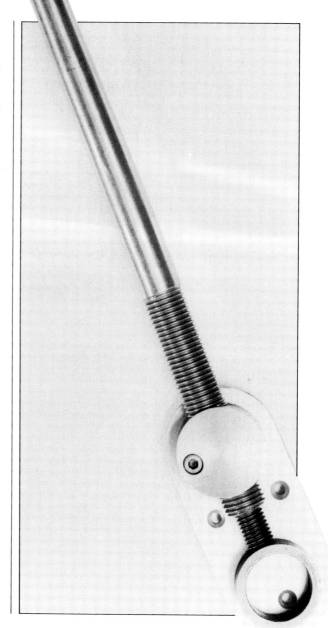

with an adjuster whose design is basically Norris. The adjuster needs its size scaling to suit the plane for which it is intended (*see* Figs 15.3 and 15.4).

The traveller – the banjo-shaped part – has to be a good fit on the head of the screw that fixes the two irons together. On single-ironed planes this traveller is modified, the circular part being replaced by a block with a pin projecting from its upper face. The pin engages into a hole in the blade. Blades made for this type of adjuster have a series of holes drilled down their centre line: as the iron wears away with constant sharpening, the pin engages the next hole in the line. The pin must be a good fit in the hole, as any play will show up as backlash in the adjustment.

The swivel has a slot cut in one side, with a small Allen screw passing through it. Clearance on the stem thread can be adjusted by tightening or slackening the Allen screw.

From the descriptions given above, and referring to the drawings and photographs, you should be able to design any adjuster to suit your purpose. The equipment you have will of course have to be taken into account.

ALL IS NOT LOST
If you are in the unfortunate position of not being able to make an adjuster, Bristol Designs sell a copy of the Norris (*see* page 155 for address).

Stanley 52 Board & Plane

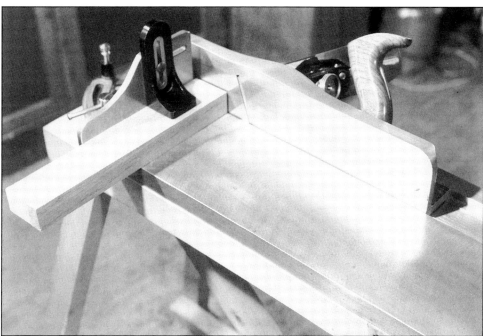

Fig 16.1 *My plane and shooting board, based on the Stanley 51 plane and 52 board – note the hold-down on the fence.*

THE ORIGINAL

Sometimes called a jack board or shooting board, and equipped with a plane designed especially to run on it, this is a most desirable tool. Stanley made this tool from 1905 until 1943, but there are very few of them about, and when they do appear at auction they command a very high price. Most of those that I have been able to inspect have been well worn or have had parts missing; the special frog seems particularly vulnerable to breakage. I once worked for a period in a workshop

121

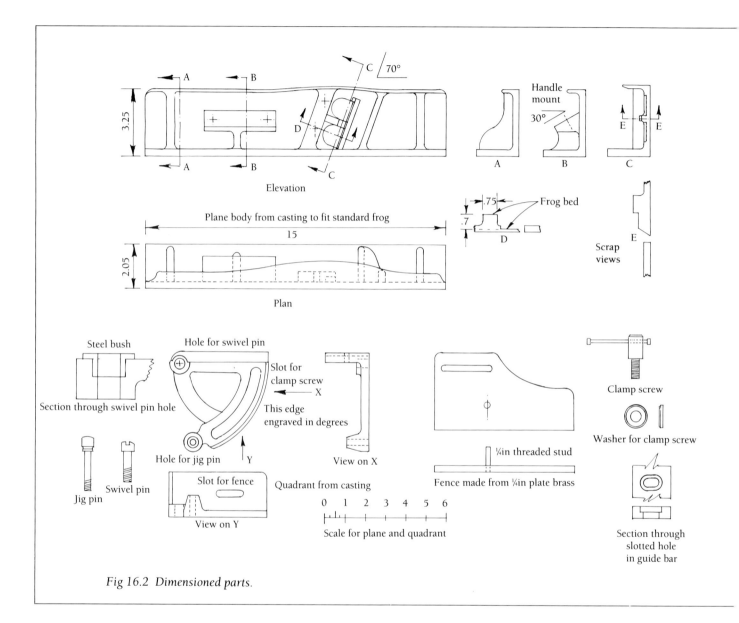

Fig 16.2 Dimensioned parts.

where there was one of these tools provided for general use. It was so useful that I decided that one day I would make myself an improved copy. So, before leaving that employer, all the details that would be needed to make one were taken down. My plane's body would be cast from a hard bronze, not the brittle cast iron of the original. The board would be made from 1in thick mild steel plate

– the original board was cast iron and ribbed to try to preserve its flatness. The quadrant that supported the fence would also be a bronze casting. The fence itself would be cut from ⅜in brass plate.

When researching the plane in old Stanley catalogues, I saw that a hold-down attached to the fence was illustrated. This part was missing from all the examples I had examined,

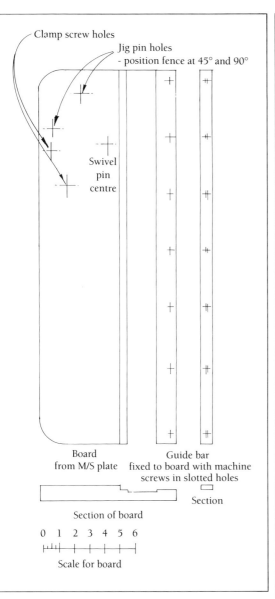

Clamp screw holes

Jig pin holes
- position fence at 45° and 90°

Swivel
pin
centre

Board
from M/S plate

Guide bar
fixed to board with machine
screws in slotted holes

Section

Section of board

0 1 2 3 4 5 6

Scale for board

and seemed a useful accessory, so I included it in my version (*see* Fig 16.1). Armed with all this information, I set to, designed and made the plane described here (*see* Fig 16.2).

PATTERNS

Three castings are required, and all three need patterns (*see* Chapter 7). The quadrant supporting the fence is the most complex of

the three, but should not pose a problem to a reasonably proficient woodworker. It will be cast upside down, so the bevels allowing the pattern to be withdrawn from the sand will need to taper towards the top.

The plane's body will be cast with the sole uppermost – do not forget to put a rapping plate in the pattern. Having had several plane bodies cast, I have found that it is best to ignore the mouth opening when making the pattern: a much better method is to cut the mouth through after casting. Even allowing for the extra metal round the mouth when the opening is included in the pattern, the casting seems to have a stress point, and after casting, the body warps at the point where the mouth opening is positioned.

The pattern for the hold-down is made so it may be cast with the flat surface fitting on to the fence at the top. The long slot is best left out of the pattern – this will make the moulder's job much easier, and the slot can easily be made in the finished casting.

THE FROG

There is a special frog fitted to the original tool made by Stanley, and this is a weak point in the tool. To be fair, all the specimens that I have been able to inspect have seen out several generations of craftsmen. However, my plane is designed around a standard 2⅜in frog; replacement frogs for Bailey pattern planes are made by both Stanley and Record. Tool shops do not hold these in stock, but will order one for you.

The frog will need a slight modification made to it: the side should be filed to fit under the top flange of the body. The body itself has been altered from the original design – the original had a flat top flange, while in my version there is a bump in its centre which allows it to pass unbroken over the frog.

A lever cap can be ordered at the same time as the frog. Make sure that the frog is bought with the screw that holds the irons and lever cap, as in some catalogues this is listed as a separate part. If you do not have a ready supply of machine screws, the two that hold the frog to the body can also be purchased with the frog; a set of taps, with a thread to suit these two screws, will be needed.

THE BODY

Finishing the casting for the body follows the same procedure as that previously explained for other planes. However, there are one or two things that are worthy of special mention: the sole and the flange (the part of the body that runs on the bed) need to be at right angles to one another. Particular attention should be paid to this if the tool is to work to its full potential. The flange not only runs on the bed but also runs between guides, and will therefore have to be perfectly parallel in width,

Fig 16.3 Plane and board, showing the guide strip and recessed Allen screws.

or it will not run true.

When fitting the frog to the body, make sure that there is sufficient room to move it back and forth to adjust the width of the mouth. The inside of the body looks best if finished with black paint; I had mine stove-enamelled, which contrasts with the bronze and makes a very pretty plane.

THE BOARD

This is one part that I had to have made by a local engineering firm. The shaped rebate is a job that needs a milling machine, and a substantial one at that, so I went along with my drawing and got a price for them to supply the material and make the part. Only the board need be purchased this way, as the guide strip can be made and fitted to it quite easily.

The guide strip is fitted to the board with recessed Allen screws, which fit into slots to enable the strip to be adjusted to make a good running fit on the flange of the plane's body (see Fig 16.3). When I first finished my plane I lubricated the slideway with oil – this was a mistake. The fine dust from planing end grain mixed with the oil and made a thick paste in which the plane had difficulty moving. Powdered graphite is the best lubricant for this purpose. There is no need to purchase it especially, as a soft pencil rubbed on abrasive paper will produce sufficient for the purpose: the graphite embeds in the surface of the metal, reducing friction and wear.

The board will need drilling very accurately for the quadrant, and the holes should be set out very carefully: there is the main hole for the swivel pin of the quadrant, which will also have to be tapped. The other holes are for the locking screw, and two for the locating pin. You may find that it is best to drill and tap the hole for the swivel pin first. The quadrant can then be mounted, set at 90°

to the plane's sole and the locating pinhole marked; the same can be done for the 45° setting. The positions of the holes for the locking screw are not quite so important, and there can be a little tolerance in their positioning.

THE QUADRANT

The raw casting will need filing, so first make the underside that fits on to the board true. The face to which the fence is attached should then be made flat and at a true 90° to the finished underside. The curved slot in which the clamping screw runs will need cleaning up, and other surfaces should have any casting marks removed. The holes for the swivel and locating pin are then drilled: as these holes need to be a good fit on the parts that fit into them, they may need reaming. If you do not have a reamer, the hole could be drilled first and then the part made to fit the hole.

I keep my eyes open when I visit a local scrapyard; the firm that owns it has contracts with several manufacturers to remove their scrap, and by visiting the scrapyard from time to time, I collect any pieces of metal that are large enough for further use. There are often interesting wingnuts, knurled knobs and other goodies to be had. The proprietor weighs whatever I have gleaned, and I am charged the scrap rate plus 25% for it. Most of the pins, nuts and bolts that I use on my tools are acquired in this way. Another good source for odds and ends is Whistons (see Appendix).

On my shooting board, both the swivel and the locating pin were turned for me by a friend, while the clamping bolt was recovered from scrap. The tapped hole for the swivel pin must be made exactly perpendicular to the surface of the board – if it is the slightest amount out, the quadrant will not swing properly on the pin.

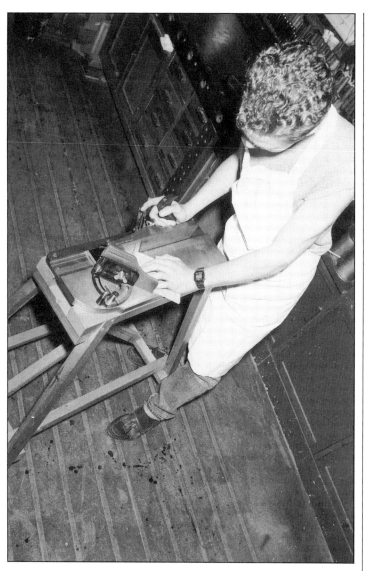

Fig 16.4 Board and plane in use on specially made stand.

THE FENCE AND HOLD-DOWN

The fence is cut from a piece of ⅜in thick plate brass; if you have difficulty obtaining brass, mild steel will suffice. I used brass because it will not rust, and the hands come into contact with the fence a lot during use. A hole for the stud by which the fence is attached to the

quadrant is drilled and tapped. When the stud is fitted, it is best secured into the fence with Loctite. There is a slot cut in the fence for the hold-down bolt; finishing the hold-down is a simple job of filing the two faces true and cutting the slot.

Apart from the flat working surfaces, both the quadrant and the hold-down are finished to match the inside of the body. The quadrant can be engraved with a scale showing degrees, useful when angles other than 90° or 45° are to be worked.

FINISHING TOUCHES

Details of making and fitting handles are given in Chapter 22, which also provides all the information needed to handle this plane. If you want to personalize your plane, have your name engraved on it in the space on the quadrant and top flange. I collect old cast lever caps that are bare of all engraving: when these have been polished I have my name engraved on them, and this really does finish off the plane nicely.

The finished tool is very heavy and not the kind of thing that you will want to keep moving about. You will see from Fig 16.4 that I have mounted mine on a stand, which puts it at just the right height to use. Once you have one of these tools, you will find that it is called into use far more than you originally thought it would be.

The only parts that have not been mentioned so far are the irons. A standard proprietary blade and back iron will suffice: I have a 'Samurai' brand Japanese blade in my plane, and can recommend this blade as the sharp edge lasts twice as long as that of the standard blade. Unfortunately it is the same thickness and can have the same chatter problem as the standard blade when working on difficult wood.

Brass & Steel Mitre Plane

Fig 17.1 *The finished mitre plane.*

17

This chapter completes my description of plane making: from the information contained in this and previous chapters, the design and making of any plane can be contemplated. The plane included here has several principles not previously covered, while those already explained are not repeated. Therefore, if you are proposing to make this plane, re-read the previous chapters on plane making.

DESCRIPTION

This is a very low-angled plane, suitable for working on end grain (*see* Fig 17.1). As the plane is used in the hand, the sides are brass to prevent rusting. The iron is thick and heavy and held down firmly under the wedge,

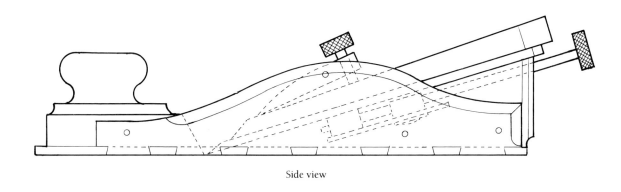

Side view

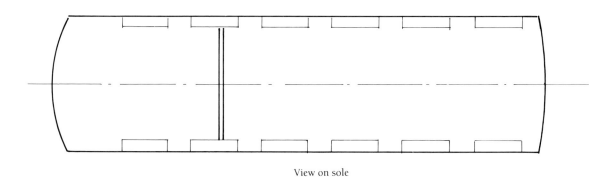

View on sole

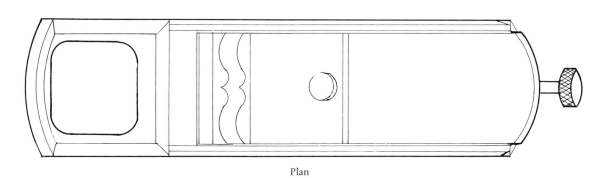

Plan

Fig 17.2 Dimensioned parts.

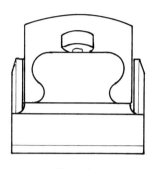

Front view

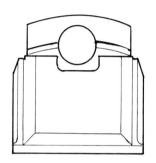

Back view

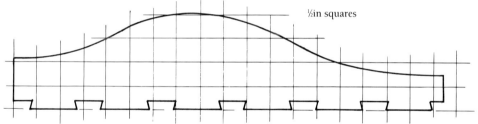

½in squares

Template for side, cut from ¼ in brass plate

Front

4 screw holes

Plate

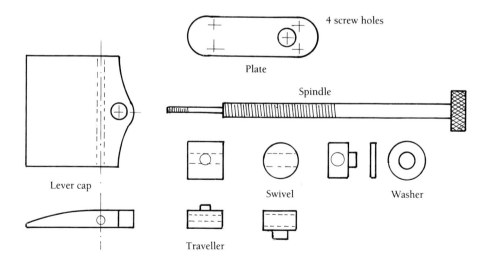

Lever cap

Spindle

Swivel

Washer

Traveller

making the plane an ideal tool for use on precision work – shavings as thin as 1½thou can be made with it.

I am not aware of an identical commercially-made plane ever having been produced. I have a fine mitre plane by Mathieson and Son, but it has a much steeper-pitched iron than that described here.

THE BODY

This body is dovetailed together, but differs from those already described in that the dovetails are only splayed in one direction. They are similar to the conventional tail used in woodworking, except that the angle is much steeper. The tails are set out in Fig 17.2. As the sides of the plane are so shallow, the rivets will hold them together. The dovetails have only to hold the sole on, and the tails should be made an interference fit in their sockets, i.e. about a thou oversize. The sharp inside corners of the tails are removed so that they will start into the sockets.

When, after some trial and fitting, it is seen that the sides will go on to the sole, the assembly is forced together by cramping in the vice. Place a strip of thick steel on either side of the body to spread the load and prevent marking when cramping. Once these parts are assembled they cannot be taken apart, so it is important that all work done before assembly is completed before cramping up.

INFILL AND WEDGE

The infill and front cushion knob are made and fitted as explained previously. The position of the rivets in the rear infill needs careful positioning: there is little space for them, as they must not foul the adjuster mechanism.

The wedge is an important part of the plane – not only is the top end a handle, but it keeps the iron down firmly on the bed. To help in this function there are two strips of ¼in thick steel bar housed in its underside; the steel also adds weight to the plane, helping to make it work smoothly. A strip of brass inlaid in the face of the wedge prevents the lever cap screw from causing damage.

The adjuster is a modified version of a Norris blade adjuster, explained fully in Chapter 15. The stem needs to be made of a length that will allow the knob to clear the top of the wedge.

Superior Marking Gauges

Fig 18.1 *The finished standard Mark II marking gauge.*

A VERY OLD TOOL

Marking gauges have been around for quite some while; the oldest reference to them is in *Principes de l'Architecture* by A. Felibien, Paris 1676, so there is proof that they have a history of over 300 years. Now, you would think anything that old would have been refined down until it could not be improved further. As explained in Chapter 1, I found a need that had not been met. In fact, I found several.

In my workshop there must have been at least two dozen marking gauges, some made from wood and others from various metals. All these gauges felt clumsy when used on fine small work. I often undertake repairs on old mahogany cameras, where the tolerance that one needs to work to is very small and many parts have to slide against one another but remain light-tight. There was a need for something small and accurate. In addition, the

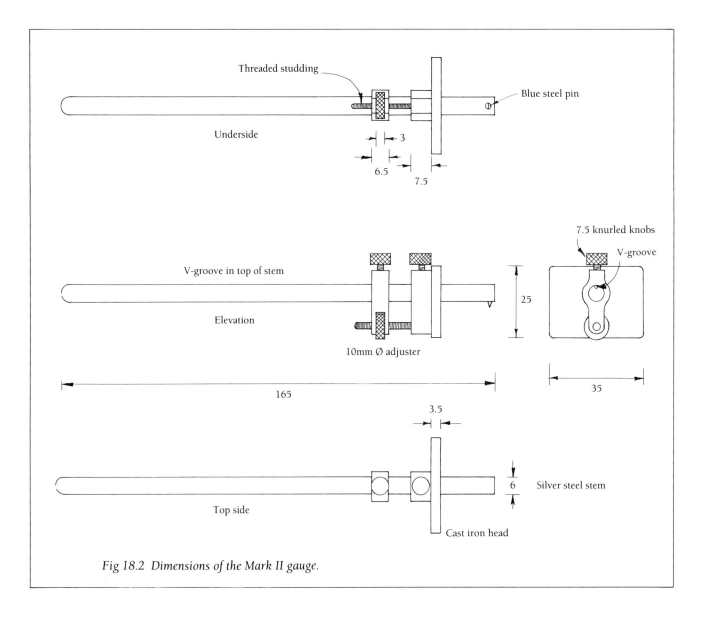

Fig 18.2 *Dimensions of the Mark II gauge.*

gauges I owned always seemed so clumsy when working on quality cabinetmaking.

THREE DIFFERENT DESIGNS

The making of three totally different gauges will be explained. They each have a different use, and you must decide what is required for the type of work you undertake. The first is a replacement for the standard marking gauge: the finished gauge turned out bigger than I

had imagined it (*see* Fig 18.1). This is quite often a problem when making tools from scratch – a tool can look quite different in size from a two-dimensional drawing to the finished item.

However, this gauge, although originally intended for small work, has turned out to be very useful as a general marking gauge. It has a knurled roller working on a fine thread to set the adjustment, and is far more accurate than the standard wooden marking gauge.

Fig 18.2 shows all the dimensions of the gauge; these can of course be modified to suit your particular need. The head is made from round bar – chunks too short for industrial needs can be found amongst scrap, and firms that supply model makers offer short lengths (*see* page 155). To reduce the weight, the back of the head is turned down in diameter; this also facilitates the handling of the gauge. The head could be fabricated by soldering two pieces of brass of different diameters together.

The stem is a length of ground silver steel. To prevent the head and slider from rotating around the stem, a groove the full length of the stem, in which the locking screws locate, is made. If you have a problem making the groove, a flat will suffice; this can easily be formed with a file.

The wheel that acts as a cutter was used instead of a pin; this was experimental, and I thought at the time that it would be less likely to follow the grain. However, it is quite useful as, no matter which way the gauge is picked up, it can be applied directly to the wood without having to look for the pin. The cutting wheel is made glass hard, and does not need tempering. A small 8BA bolt holds the wheel on to the end of the stem, which has its end tapped to receive the bolt. The bolt is fixed in its final position when the wheel can rotate freely without sideways play. Loctite prevents the bolt from unscrewing when the gauge is used.

The slide into which the knurled roller fits is filed to shape from a piece of brass bar. The roller must be a good fit lengthwise in the slider: any play will show up in the adjustment, which will not be positive. Both the holes in the slider and the head should be an easy fit on the stem. Lengths of screwed rod called studding can be purchased, and this is very useful stuff. The adjuster screw is made

from a short length of studding; choose a fine pitched thread and remember you must have a tap of the same thread.

The end of the screwed rod is attached to the head by a small block, which is drilled and tapped to fit on the end of the rod. Hard solder is then used to attach the block to the head; this needs to be done very carefully, as the rod must be in perfect alignment with the stem. To achieve this alignment, leave the soldering until all the parts are made, then fit the head and slider on to the stem and feed the screwed rod through the knurled roller in the slider. This will hold the rod in position while it is being soldered. Allow the solder to flow around the thread where it enters the small brass block; this will prevent it from coming unscrewed in use.

This brass gauge is quite a heavy tool. It has been suggested to me that it would be an improvement if it had been made from aluminium – personally I do not mind the weight, and there is a problem when it comes to soldering aluminium.

THE PRECISION MARKING GAUGE

I explained in Chapter 1 how this gauge came to be designed and made: it is one of my favourite tools, fulfilling to perfection all the purposes for which it was designed. I must admit that I designed it but did not make it; the gauge was made for me by a close friend, a very fine craftsman, as a special gift. This gentleman was nearing retirement, having worked as an instrument maker all his life. I think of him every time I use it.

I will explain how I would go about making this tool with the limited resources in my workshop. The original head and slider were machined from a solid block of fine grey cast iron. This is impossible without very specialized machinery. I would make patterns and have these two parts cast, probably from gunmetal or another hard bronze, depending on what the foundry could offer me. The holes would not be included in the patterns, but drilled in the castings after their faces had been made true.

The screwed rod is fitted into a tapped hole in the head; the drilling and tapping needs to be done very accurately if the adjustment is to work freely. This is done by assembling the slider and head together on a short bar the same diameter as the stem. These two parts are positioned tight together in correct orientation. A drill is then passed through the pilot hole in the slider and the head drilled – as the two holes are of different finished sizes, an undersized drill would be used to form the pilot holes in both parts. The pilot holes would be opened up afterwards with drills of the correct size.

The pin is made of blue steel, a high carbon steel used by clock and instrument makers. The pin fits into a hole in the stem, where there is a slot sawn through the hole from the end of the stem. The pin is oversize for its hole and forces the slot open slightly, which then grips the pin firmly. The marking gauge works best if the pin is sharpened to a knife edge and not a point.

The rest of the manufacture of this gauge follows the same principles as those given for the brass gauge. With a fine precision tool such as this, it is worth making a fitted box in which it can be stored when not in use.

MINIATURE GAUGES

For very small work I need miniature gauges that will work to very precise dimensions. The heads are identical to those of the full-sized gauge, and are made from aluminium. They are turned on the lathe from plate, but could easily be fabricated: a square piece of sheet could be riveted to a short piece of round bar.

The stem of the marking gauge is similar to that described above for the precision gauge. The mortice gauge has a second pin attached to a small movable plate recessed into the stem (*see* Fig 18.2).

These are very simple tools, but that does not mean that they can be knocked up quickly. If they are to fill the purpose for which they are designed, they need to be made very accurately – this particularly applies to the movable pin in the mortice gauge.

Forge Work & Screwdrivers

19

FORGE WORK

There is a very satisfying feeling to be gained from taking a piece of red-hot, glowing metal and beating it into the shape of a tool. One of the simplest tools that we use, the screwdriver, can easily be made this way. There is no need to purchase expensive new material; a visit to the car breakers will supply most of our needs. The springs from the suspension of scrapped vehicles make fine tools, while engine pushrods are an inexpensive source of thin round steel bar.

Coil springs may not look as though any tool could be made from them, but once heated to bright red they can be straightened, and there is a bar of good quality carbon steel. Leaf springs can be used to forge chisels and turning tools. There are many suitable pieces of metal lying about in a breakers' yard, just waiting to be re-used (see Fig 19.1).

EQUIPMENT

Methods of heating metal have already been discussed in Chapter 4. Something that can act as an anvil will be required; a short bit of railway rail or girder will do. Record make a series of small anvils, the largest of which is an ideal, and moderately priced tool (see Fig 19.2). When you have gained a little experience, tongs to hold the hot metal can be forged quite simply. Until then, you will need something with which to hold the hot metal. Any large pliers or pincers will do. Make sure they are old, as the heat will ruin them for their original use.

Protective clothing is essential. The minimum requirement is: a pair of good industrial **gloves**; stout **footwear**, preferably safety boots; eye protection – **goggles** are better than glasses; **overalls** that are not inflammable – the very best protection here is a long leather **apron**; as sparks can fly a

Fig 19.1 The proceeds of one trip to the scrapyard: brass knurled knobs, steel rod, brass tube, old files, sheet steel, brass bar and a high tensile bolt.

considerable distance, some form of **hat** is advisable. It is important to take pains over acquiring this clothing. You need to be comfortable and at ease when wearing it, or there will be a tendency to do without it.

SOMETHING SIMPLE TO START WITH

To get the feeling and to build up your confidence, make something very simple to start with. A screwdriver of the pattern known as an electrician's is ideal. A bar of metal the diameter of the finished tool and the length of the blade is required. Working in subdued

lighting (so that the colour of the metal can be judged accurately), heat one end of the bar to bright red, holding the other end in the tongs. The heated end is held on the anvil and the taper is formed by beating on both sides with a hammer.

There is a good deal of skill in judging the correct heat and in the use of the hammer. As with all skills, these are only acquired by experience and practice; if you are using scrap material, the only expense is the heat. Experiment by getting the metal to different temperatures; this is judged by the brightness of the colour. The old saying, 'Practice makes perfect', very aptly applies here.

During forging, the material needs to be moved constantly on the anvil. The hammer is forming the shape of the finished item, which must be continuously judged by eye. The metal will quickly lose its heat, so some speed is needed; even so, repeated heating will be required. Do not be tempted into trying to work chilled metal. An old blacksmith from whom I learnt quite a lot would often remark, 'A man who works cold metal makes a job for the blacksmith who works hot metal.'

A word of warning – do not heat high carbon steel beyond bright red, as excessive heating robs it of its carbon content. You will know when this happens, as the metal will crumble under the hammer. The steel is then in a condition known as burnt, and is useless.

Once you have forged the taper, heat the other end of the rod. This time forge a long square point to act as a tang. While the metal is still red-hot, take a cold chisel and cut some barbs on the tang. Incidentally, metal bar can easily be cut with a cold chisel when red-hot – this method is quicker and much easier than using a hacksaw.

Some final shaping of the tip of the blade may need to be done on the grinder. The blade of the screwdriver must be heat-treated. Only the tip that engages the screw slot need be hardened. (Heat treatment is explained in Chapter 6.) The finished blade is cleaned and polished with emery cloth to remove the surface colours. All that is needed now is a handle, and the tool is finished.

FORGING TECHNIQUES

Having carried out the simple task outlined above, you will have some idea of what is involved in forging. Before you will be able to make anything worthwhile, there are two forging operations that must be mastered. The first is known as **drawing down**: this is a thinning of the metal, i.e. reducing the diameter of a bar. The work, heated to working temperature, is placed on a slightly rounded surface (the back of the anvil) and struck hard and repeatedly, the metal being constantly turned between hammer blows. When the desired size is reached the work is moved on to a flat surface, and all irregularities in the metal are removed with lighter hammer blows.

When drawing down round stock it is usual to beat it square, then octagonal and finally back to round. No matter what final cross-section is required, it is usual to draw the metal down as a square. Trying to draw down keeping the rod round is almost an impossibility, and the work becomes very misshapen in section.

Upsetting or **jumping up** is the opposite to drawing down; it refers to thickening the cross-section of the stock, and is a far more difficult process. It is therefore a better plan, when working a tool with irregular sections, to start with a thick bar and draw down the thin parts. Starting with a thin bar and trying to upset the thick parts is very difficult.

Upsetting involves beating the metal endwise – this is not too difficult on short

Fig 19.2 Anvil.

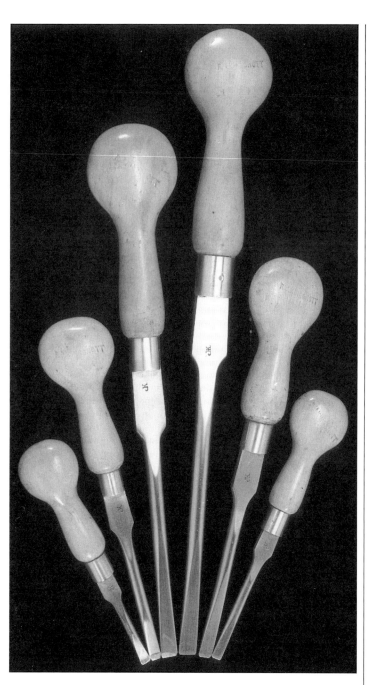

Fig 19.3 The finished set of screwdrivers.

work, but long pieces tend to bend. Upsetting should be practised on thick stock; the rules are: work hot, hit it hard and keep it straight.

A SET OF SCREWDRIVERS

I gave up in despair trying to find a decent screwdriver in the shops. The ones I had been using had seen better days – they were secondhand when I got them 45 years ago: the most popular sizes had been used almost every day, and the tips had been reground countless times. The handles were those good old carved ones that are no longer made, and all the new drivers in the tool shop had plastic handles – yuk! So I set to and made the set illustrated here (*see* Fig 19.3).

Each different gauge of screw requires a different screwdriver. It is possible to manage with less, but while you are about it why not make a full set? The average screwdriver is misused; it is used as a lever to pry joints apart, and to open paint cans, not its purpose at all. Having made this set of fine tools, you can relegate your old drivers to the more mundane tasks.

Close inspection of the photographs will reveal the shape of the blades; they are all the same shape, but vary in size. As previously explained, one works by eye when forging, so it is important to get the shape fixed well and truly in your mind's eye before starting.

Bigger blades are easier to forge than small ones, so I suggest you make the biggest first. Mine are made from old coil springs from a car; the bar when straightened was somewhat thicker than the centre round part of the blade, as the wide end near the ferrule has quite a lot of metal in it.

The end with the tang on it is forged first – this is just a matter of beating the metal down from both sides to form the flat section. The round part of the blade will need drawing down to the correct diameter. The tip is forged last and should be slightly wider than the round part of the blade. There are special tools called swages which blacksmiths use for finishing round sections. These help, but are not essential.

A certain amount of grinding and filing will be needed to bring the blade to its final shape, and polishing with various grades of emery paper will remove all signs of marks made during forging. Make sure that the tip is exactly right – this is the part where most screwdrivers fall down. Get a screw of the correct gauge, made to British Standard Specification 1210. The blade should fit the slot perfectly and needs to be slightly wider than the screw as the corners of the tip are removed. The thickness should just allow it to enter the slot, but there should be no play. A screwdriver that is thinner than required will enter the slot easily, but in use only the two extreme edges will transfer the twisting force to the screw. This small area of contact is the prime reason for the mess that can be made to the screw heads by some drivers, and you can

see why a separate screwdriver is needed for each size of screw.

Apart from heat treatment, the screwdriver blade is finished. As much care is needed in heat-treating the blade as would be expended on the finest cutting tool. There is a tendency by some woodworkers to underrate the importance of the screwdriver. If the blade is too soft the tip will very soon become misshapen; on the other hand, if it is too hard it will be brittle, and the corners of the tip will break off. Only the tip needs to be hardened and tempered.

FINISHING TOUCHES
Polish the blade until all tool marks are removed, and the surface is smooth and shiny. Handles are described in Chapter 22, but before fitting one put your mark on the flat part of the blade: having taken the trouble to make the tool, you should personalize it.

Once you have mastered the art of forge work, the potential for making many different tools is opened up and it is only limited by your imagination and ingenuity.

Modifications to the Bench Vice

20

THERE ARE VICES AND VICES

Over the years many different patterns of woodworking vice have been manufactured. Some are more efficient than others, but the efficiency of all of them can be affected by the way they are attached to the bench. As with all woodworking, each individual craftsman has his own likes and dislikes, and I can only tell you about mine. Over the years I have worked at many benches, and the vices have varied from old ones with a wooden screw to the latest quick-release pattern. So when I made a new bench for my own workshop, I had all this experience to draw upon (*see* Fig 20.2).

WHERE?

Where on the bench will the vice be fitted? This may seem a silly question, because by tradition it always goes on the left-hand front end of the bench. That is fine for the right-handed worker, but what if he or she is left-handed? Would it not be better if the vice was moved to the other end of the bench? Having decided where on the bench the vice is going to be located, we must decide at what height it will be positioned (*see* Fig 20.1).

The vice can be fitted with the top of its jaws level with the top of the bench, which means that there is metal exposed at the working level. This is a nuisance when sawing etc., as the tool can easily foul the metal. A much better practice is to keep the vice about 1in down from the bench top.

All vices should have wooden jaws inside the metal ones. These are kept up level with the bench top, are fitted to project above the top and are then planed down after fitting. The outside wooden jaw is recessed so that the metal vice jaw is housed inside it. This is much kinder to the tools, as it is almost impossible to knock them on the metal parts of the vice.

These wooden vice jaws have a rebate worked on their ends. This enables an inner removable pad to be fitted (*see* Fig 20.3). Several sets of these removable pads are made, each with a different material glued to its working surface. The pads used for general woodwork have hardboard with the pattern side outwards, while another set is lined with upholstery felt, and is ideal for holding finished work without marking it. For difficult items that might spoil the face of the pads, a pair with metal linings is used (*see* Fig 20.4).

SHAPED WORK

Holding shaped work in the vice usually poses some problems. A special set of pad inserts is used with blocks shaped to fit the part to be held screwed to the inserts. When working long lengths of wood, there may be a problem holding the free end of the work piece: it is quite simple to support this by a peg fitted into the bench leg at the opposite end to the vice. A series of holes can be bored in the leg so that the peg can be adjusted to suit the width of the wood. However, as the vice jaw stands proud of the bench edge, the end of the wood can still move about, so a small attachment is made to fit on the bench and steady the end of the timber.

THE TAIL VICE

There is a type of bench that has become known as a cabinetmaker's bench. This piece of equipment originates from Denmark, where it is known as a *snickärbank*. It is fitted with a tail vice, which is an integral part of the bench. Several firms make the screw for this type of vice; the rest of the mechanism is

Fig 20.1 *General view of a cabinetmaker's bench, showing tail vice and softening pads fitted to front vice.*

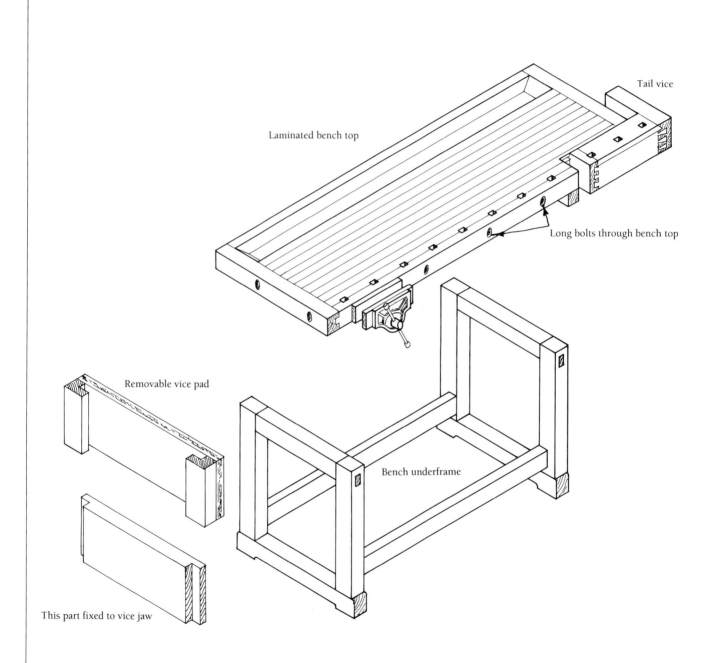

Tail vice

Laminated bench top

Long bolts through bench top

Removable vice pad

Bench underframe

This part fixed to vice jaw

Fig 20.2 Plan of the bench and detail of tail vice.

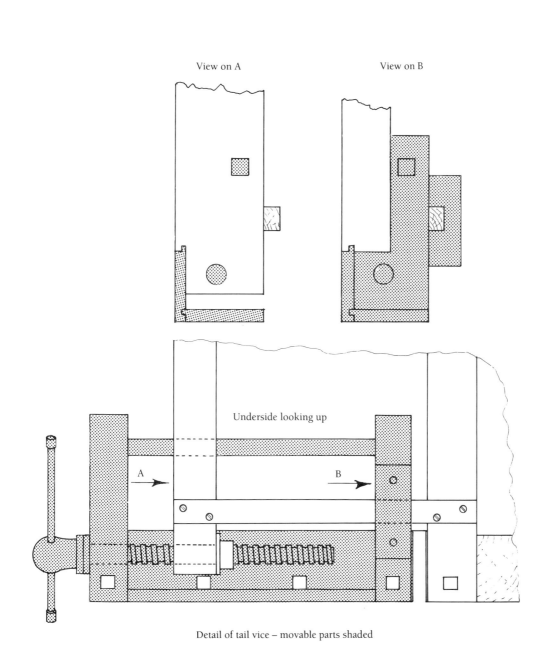

View on A

View on B

Underside looking up

A

B

Detail of tail vice – movable parts shaded

Fig 20.3 Removable pads being fitted to vice.

wooden and is constructed at the same time as the bench. A proficient woodworker should have little difficulty in constructing a bench incorporating this vice, using the illustrations as guides. Because of the moving parts, the timber used should be a stable hardwood, dry and well-seasoned.

A little tip I think well worth passing on concerns the bar that passes through the vice screw and is used to tighten or loosen the jaws. When used and left with most of its length above the screw, it slides down and the knob on the end of the bar bangs on to the head of the screw with a loud noise. This spoils the peace of the workshop and is distracting when one's attention is fully engaged on the work in hand. A felt washer can be fitted under the head of each knob (*see* Fig 20.4), and peace reigns in the workshop.

Fig 20.4 Removable pads – note the rebated linings fitted to the vice. Left to right: hardboard faced, abrasive paper faced, upholsterers' felt faced, plain wood.

Knives

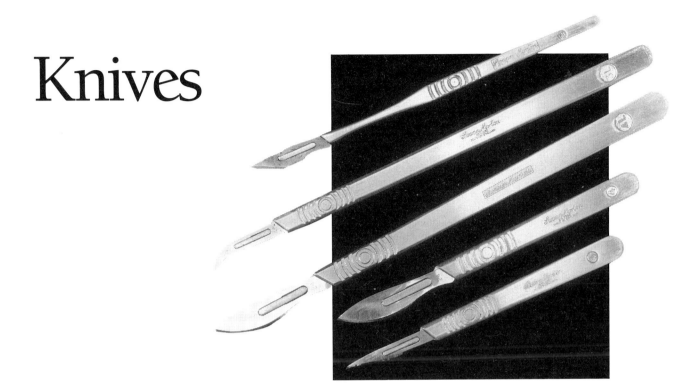

Fig 21.1 Surgical scalpels by Swan Morton.

21

In the *Dictionary of Tools*, R.A.Salaman states, 'The ordinary Knife is not much used by the woodworking trade'; this is perhaps because suitable knives are not available. I notice that almost every craftsman that I know owns a Stanley craft knife; the Swan Morton surgical scalpel has also become a standard tool, and a very useful one at that (*see* Fig 21.1). For some years I have made and used knives for several applications.

The design of the knife varies over quite a wide field. A delicate tool held like a pen and used to make fine precise cuts, as in marquetry, is the lightest. Then there is the heavy-bladed knife held in the fist and used to make heavy cuts, as when pointing a stake. Between these two extremes there are a host of useful tools (*see* Fig 21.2).

Knives are very personal things: the shape that suits a certain person for a particular use can be ineffective in somebody else's hands.

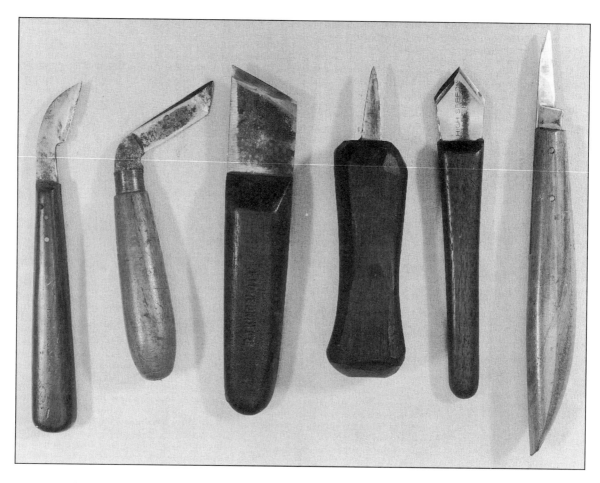

Fig 21.2 Selection of knives, each with a specific use.

The size and shape is best arrived at by trial and error; I have included photographs of some of my knives, which will give you an indication of shape and size. One good thing about making a knife is that the blade can be shaped on the grindstone, which means that it can be repeatedly modified until the ideal shape is obtained.

As with other tools that we make, the first consideration is to decide what the knife will be used for. The illustrations for this chapter show that the shape and size varies over a wide field, and that the way the knife is held plays a big part in the shape of the blade. For instance, marking out knives have the cutting edge on the end of the blade, while paring knives have the cutting edge along the blade parallel to the handle.

THE MATERIAL

Knives can be made from a variety of reclaimed pieces of steel. One of the best sources of material that I have found is old cutthroat razors – these are no longer required for their original use, and are to be found at junk sales and the like (*see* Fig 21.3). In most cases the steel in these old razors is of the very best quality, and one must take precautions not to burn and spoil the steel when reshaping these blades on the grinder.

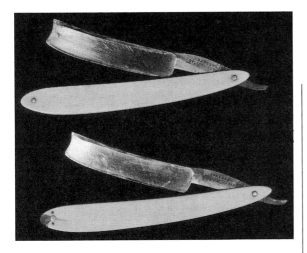

Fig 21.3 Cutthroat razors are a good source of fine steel for making knives.

Worn-out hacksaw blades make good knives; machine hacksaw blades of the larger size are also very useful, and can be used to make quite large knives. The blades from old sheath knives and penknives can be used, but beware of stainless steel, as this does not take a very sharp edge. Old files can be softened, shaped and then heat-treated; I have several favourite tools made from files.

When making knives from flat steel, or those with a flat tang, it is a good policy to rivet the handle on – individual pieces of wood are fixed either side of the blade, making a sandwich of: wood, blade, wood. Rivets then pass through all three components, holding them firmly together. This would be ideal for knives made from a hacksaw, but it is difficult to drill high-speed steel. I am told that a cobalt drill can do this, but never having used one I am unable to recommend it. I resort to making the tang of the blade rough on the grindstone, then Aralditing the handle to it.

STORING AND SHARPENING

When not in use knives are best kept stuck into a block of balsawood (*see* Fig 21.4). If they are put in a drawer, not only does the edge suffer but there is a danger of cut fingers when sorting out the knife required.

As with all woodworking cutting tools, the knife only works properly when really sharp. At least two stones will be needed; one medium, the other very fine. It is best if these stones are kept for knives only, as sharpening knives on a stone will wear it hollow. It is impossible to use the whole of the stone as with other tools, as the knife's handle is in the way. It will not affect the efficiency of the stone for sharpening knives when it has become misshapen, but it will be useless for other tools.

A leather strop to put the final touch to a sharp edge can be made. Strips of leather are glued either side of a board and treated with stropping paste: this paste comes in a stick that looks something like a wax crayon. The sticks are sold in pairs of different grades in a little box – the red one is coarser than the black one. Barbers still use cutthroat razors, and if asked nicely they will order stropping paste for you from their supplier.

Fig 21.4 Knives stuck in a block of balsa wood for storage and safety.

Handles

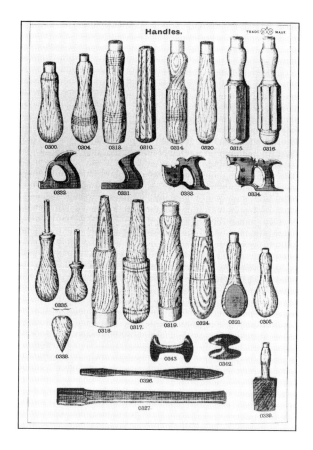

Fig 22.1 *Page from Preston's catalogue of 1901, showing the range of replacement handles readily available at that time.*

A COMMON THING

If a hand tool is to work efficiently, its handle must conform to two criteria: it must be comfortable to hold and work with, and even more importantly (and this is where many tools of recent design fall down), it must exert maximum control over the tool (*see* Fig 22.1). A couple of examples of handles that fail in this last respect come readily to mind: the mortice chisel handle that is out of line with the blade, thus cutting a mortice not square to the surface of the wood; and the modern combination plane that has undergone so much price engineering that it is an abomination to use – the handle is so shaped that the hand slides straight off the top of it (*see* Fig 22.2). All our tools are held and manipulated by the hand, so you will see just how important the handle is.

DIFFERENT TYPES

The procedure for designing a handle follows similar lines to those that have been described for designing tools. Some analysis of the tool's use, inspection of what others have done, and at least a good sketch of what is to be made, are all required. To dismiss the design and making of the handle to a lower level than that of making the tool is a serious mistake. By being consciously aware of the handle when using a tool, its good points and shortcomings can be noted, and after a while, experience will give you an idea of what constitutes a good handle.

Not only does the handle affect the work the tool does, it can also help in other ways;

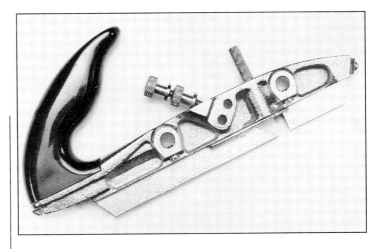

Fig 22.2 A modern combination plane with the most impractical handle imaginable. When I complained to the manufacturer, I was told that the plane had won a Design Council Award!

for instance, an octagonal London pattern chisel handle will not roll and fall on to the floor as a round handle will. With carving tools, where there are many tools on the bench at once, it is an advantage if all the handles are slightly different from one another, as it is then easy to locate the tool you require (*see* Fig 22.3).

THE NEED FOR A LATHE

While it is possible to make round handles with hand tools, the task is much simpler with a lathe. It is not difficult to contrive something that will turn a handle: even an electric drill mounted on a board with some form of spike for a tailstock will serve. With makeshift equipment it is best to rough shape the handle before attempting to turn it, as only light cuts will then be required.

CHISEL HANDLES

I have included photographs of some different designs of chisel handle (*see* Figs 22.4 and 22.5). Reference to these photographs will enable handles suitable for any chisel to be made. However, personal preference plays a big part in the choice of design, and I would suggest that at first only one handle of any design be made. This can be used and

Fig 22.3 Page from Ward & Payne's catalogue of 1911 – note the different handles for each chisel.

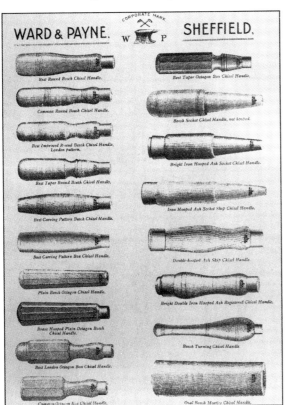

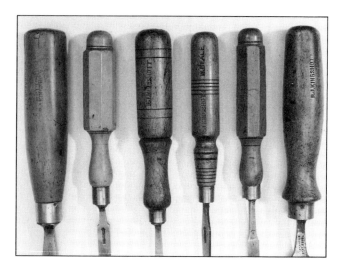

Fig 22.4 *A variety of chisel handles, all different from those supplied by today's manufacturers.*

Fig 22.5 *Chisel handles for specific uses.*

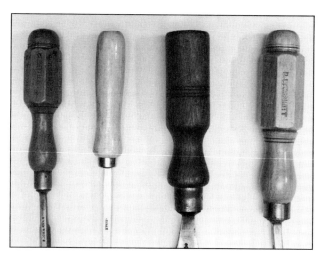

evaluated, and any alterations can then be incorporated before making more of the same pattern or even deciding that the design is not suitable for your purpose.

There are many different timbers suitable for chisel handles. The prime consideration when making a choice is, will the handle be struck with a mallet? Tools such as paring chisels, that are worked by hand pressure only, can be made from exotic hardwoods. Take care to choose a timber that will handle well and will not splinter.

Probably the most suitable wood of all is boxwood (*Buxus sempervirens*); this timber stands up well to being struck with a mallet and is very tight-grained, which makes it nice to handle. Good quality boxwood is not easy to find, and for some time now I have been using lemonwood (*Calycophyllum candidissimum*), sometimes known as degame. Most boxwood is imported from Turkey; during the Second World War there were no imports, and some manufacturers turned to false acacia (*Robinia pseudoacacia*).

Long handles for turning tools can be made from any smooth wood. Most of mine are from sycamore (*Acer pseudoplatanus*), which is low priced and can be obtained in

large sizes. I particularly like the pattern of turning handle with the knob on the end, as the knob fits comfortably into the palm of the hand and gives better control than the ordinary handle for skew chisels, scrapers and similar tools. For roughing out gouges and long and strong tools where the end of the handle is not grasped, the standard handle is to be preferred.

There will be a need for a ferrule (a metal ring) on all chisel handles. Brass is the recommended metal, and short lengths of brass tube from which ferrules can be cut can be purchased. Copper plumbers' tube can be pressed into service if brass is unavailable.

Fitting the handle on to the tang of the blade should **not** be done by heating the tang and burning it into the handle – not only will this spoil the blade's temper, but the handle will never fit properly. The method I adopt is to drill a hole using drills that get progressively smaller the further into the handle the hole goes. The size of drills can be gauged by comparing the drills to the tang.

SAW HANDLES
The difference in width between the palm of one person's hand and another's is

considerable, therefore the handle that suits one person may be the wrong size for somebody else. Not only is the handle's shape affected by the width of the hand, but the hand's length must also be considered – we have all picked up a tool and thought that the handle was far too fat or too thin. Apart from the physical size of the handle, its orientation to the blade is of prime importance; the handsaw needs particular attention paid to this feature (see Fig 22.6).

Over the years I have settled on three different patterns of saw handle: handsaw, tenon saw and dovetail. Figs 22.7, 22.8 and 22.9 show the difference between them. All my saws are fitted with one of these three patterns, and I have standard templates made from thin plywood for each handle. It is only four hours' work to produce a handle that fits my hand perfectly using one of these templates. No matter which tool I pick up, it does not feel strange because the handles on one sort of saw are all the same.

When manufacturers were producing fine tools they made the best saw handles from apple (*Malus pumila*) (see Fig 22.10); today, if we are lucky a new saw will have a beech handle, but more than likely it will be plastic. There is nothing that can be done to improve a plastic handle, except throwing it away. A new wooden handle will have been formed on a machine and can be considerably improved

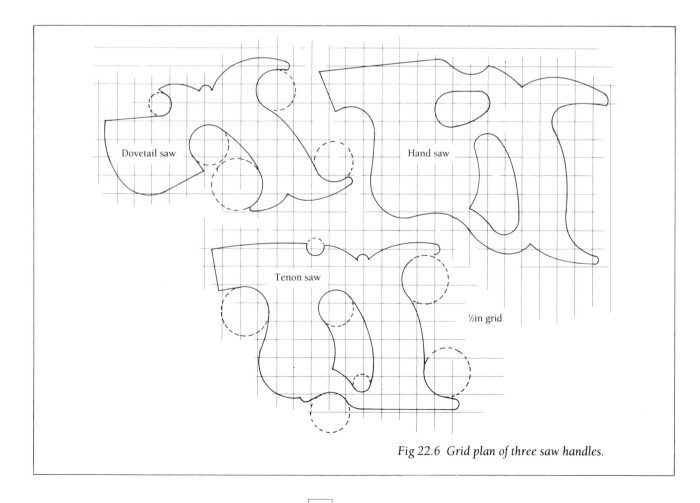

Fig 22.6 Grid plan of three saw handles.

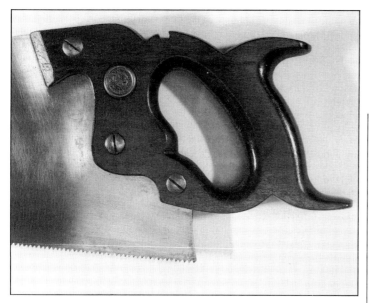

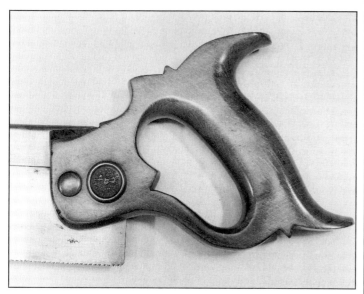

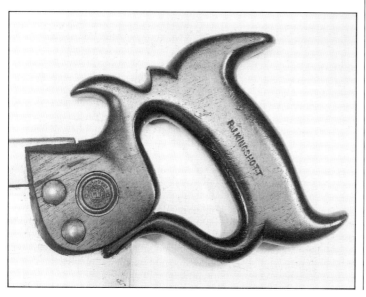

Fig 22.7 (top) Handsaw fitted with the author's pattern of handle, made from black walnut.

Fig 22.8 (middle) Dovetail saw with a closed handle, which has been reworked to remove the hard corners.

Fig 22.9 (bottom) A comfortable saw handle fitted to a very old Disston tenon saw.

with a little hand work. A rounding-over cutter will have been used to form the round inside the grip, and a hard corner is left where this round meets the flat face of the sides of the handle (*see* Fig 22.11). This is a real blister-raiser, but can easily be removed with a sharp chisel. The whole handle should be worked over with abrasive paper until all is smooth and kind to the touch.

At first sight a saw handle may look a rather difficult thing to make. Fig 22.7 shows my handsaw handle, and it will be seen that there are several true radii in its profile – these parts of a circle are all bored with a Forstner bit before cutting the outline to join them up with a bow saw. Once the handle has been cut out, the round edges are carved with a chisel.

When it comes to marking the holes for the screws that secure the blade to the handle, lay the blade on top of the handle and mark through the holes. It is possible to buy saw handle screws from some of the better tool shops. The heads of these screws have to be very carefully housed into the face of the handle – the housing must not only fit the diameter of the screw head exactly, it must also be the correct depth; inaccuracy here will spoil the appearance of an otherwise perfect handle (*see* Fig 22.12).

The finish applied to the bare wood is a matter of personal preference. I mostly give my saw handles a rub over from time to time

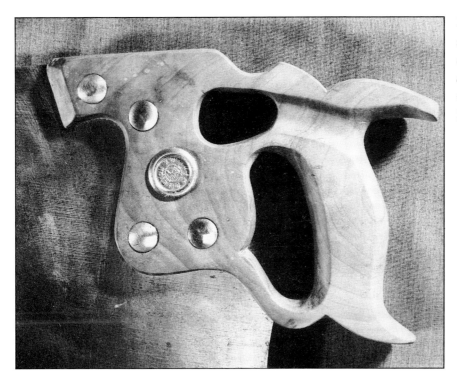

Fig 22.10 An unusual saw handle made from apple. It is very comfortable in use - one wonders why the design has not been copied.

with a linseed-oiled rag: over several years this puts on a finish that can only be achieved from lots of contact with the human skin.

PLANE HANDLES

Much of what has already been said about saw handles applies to the plane. Nearly all new Bailey pattern planes have plastic handles, and most beech-handled planes have the same hard corner discussed above. The look of a plane with a rosewood handle and knob is a great improvement over that of one fitted with stained beech: for this reason alone, without considering the improvement in handling, it is a worthwhile undertaking to make new handles. Refer to Chapter 10 for further discussion regarding the changing of handles.

My own preference of timber for plane handles is Brazilian rosewood (*Dalbergia nigra*), which, finished with French polish, was originally used on the early Stanley

Fig 22.11 Saw handle fitted by manufacturer – note the hard corners where the rounding over meets the flat side.

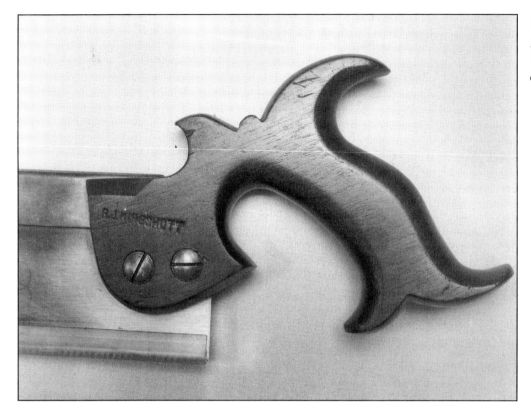

Fig 22.12 My own pattern of open saw handle, fitted to a dovetail saw.

planes, although there is some debate as to whether a modern lacquer might not be a better finish.

The hole through which the long stud passes to secure the rear handle to the body of a Bailey pattern plane needs drilling with care. Long drills suitable for this task can be purchased. I drill the hole at an early stage of making the handle, when it is just a block of wood with the profile marked upon it. In this state it is much easier to mount the wood in a vice orientated correctly for the drill.

THE PERSONAL TOUCH

Having produced a handle that has improved the tool and made it unique, why not stamp it with your name? Hardened steel name stamps are made by several companies (*see* the Appendix). If a stamp is to be used, this should be done before applying any finish, as the blow from the stamp will crack and chip any hard lacquer. While on the subject of name stamps, you may acquire secondhand tools with a previous craftsman's stamp upon them. It is considered bad form to obliterate these names; the accepted procedure in the trade is to place your stamp under that of the previous owner.

List of Suppliers

Timber

D W Beattie & Co Ltd, Dalhousie Estate, Bonnyrigg, Midlothian EH19 3HY

John Boddy's Fine Wood & Tool Store, Riverside Sawmills, Boroughbridge, North Yorkshire YO5 9LJ

Clark's Wood Co Ltd, Silverthorne Lane, St Phillips, Bristol BS2 0QJ

Karl Dazer Ltd, 163 High Street, Ongar, Essex CM5 9JD

General Woodworking Supplies, 76-80 Stoke Newington High Street, London N16 5BR

Adhesives

Hallmark Adhesives Ltd, Hoddesdon Business Centre, Brewery Road, Hoddesdon, Herts

Industrial Adhesives Ltd, Moor Road, Chesham, Bucks HP5 1SB

Evode Ltd, Common Road, Stafford, Staffs ST16 3EH

Castings

Bristol Design, 14 Perry Road, Bristol BS1 5BG

Metalworking Tools

Graham Central Tooling & Machinery, Salford House, 533/537 Lichfield Road, Aston, Birmingham B6 7SP

Chronos Ltd, 95 Victoria Street, St Albans, Herts

Metals and Solder

A J Reeves & Co (Birmingham) Ltd, Holly Lane, Marston Road, Birmingham B37 7AW

Solder

Norman Spink, 52 Highfield Lane, Newbold, Chesterfield S41 8AY

Metal

G L R Distributors Ltd, Great Northern Works, Hartham Lane, Hertford, Herts SG14 1QN

Flapstock Ltd, Shucklow Building, Little Horwood, Milton Keynes, Bucks MK17 0PT

Non-ferrous Metal

Pemmsa, Unit 6, Riverbank Enterprise Centre, Scouthill Road, Dewsbury, West Yorkshire WF13 3RQ

William Gabb Ltd, 111 Pope Street, Hockley, Birmingham

Vulcan Metals Ltd, 27 Colvilles Place, Kelvin Industrial Estate, East Kilbride G75 0PZ

Nuts, Bolts, Bits and Bobs

K R Whiston Ltd, New Mills, Stockport, Cheshire

Marking Stamps

Alan Davey, 1 Marina Drive, Brixham, Devon TQ5 9AZ

Metric Conversion Table

Inches to millimetres

¼in	6mm	6in	150mm	26in	660mm
⅜in	10mm	6⅛in	155mm	27in	685mm
½in	13mm	6¼in	160mm	28in	710mm
⅝in	16mm	6½in	165mm	29in	735mm
¾in	19mm	6¾in	170mm	30in	760mm
⅞in	22mm	7in	178mm	31in	785mm
1in	25mm	7⅛in	180mm	32in	815mm
1⅛in	30mm	7¼in	185mm	33in	840mm
1¼in	32mm	7½in	190mm	34in	865mm
1⅜in	35mm	7¾in	195mm	35in	890mm
1½in	38mm	8in	200mm	36in	915mm
1⅝in	40mm	8¼in	210mm	37in	940mm
1¾in	45mm	8½in	215mm	38in	965mm
2in	50mm	8¾in	220mm	39in	990mm
2⅛-2¼in	55mm	9in	230mm	40in	1015mm
2⅜in	60mm	9¼in	235mm	41in	1040mm
2½in	63mm	9½in	240mm	42in	1065mm
2⅝in	65mm	9¾in	250mm	43in	1090mm
2¾in	70mm	10in	255mm	44in	1120mm
3in	75mm	10⅛in	257mm	45in	1145mm
3⅛in	80mm	11in	280mm	46in	1170mm
3¼in	83mm	12in	305mm	47in	1195mm
3½in	88mm	13in	330mm	48in	1220mm
3⅔in	93mm	14in	355mm	49in	1245mm
3¾in	95mm	15in	380mm	50in	1270mm
4in	100mm	16in	405mm	51in	1295mm
4⅛in	105mm	17in	430mm	52in	1320mm
4¼-4⅜in	110mm	18in	460mm	53in	1345mm
4½in	115mm	19in	485mm	54in	1370mm
4¾in	120mm	20in	510mm	55in	1395mm
5in	125mm	21in	535mm	56in	1420mm
5⅛in	130mm	22in	560mm	57in	1450mm
5¼in	133mm	23in	585mm	58in	1475mm
5½in	140mm	24in	610mm	59in	1500mm
5¾in	145mm	25in	635mm	60in	1525mm

To obtain the metric size for dimensions under 60in not shown in the above table, multiply the imperial size in inches by 25.4 and round to the nearest millimetre, taking 0.5mm upwards.

e.g. 9⅛in x 25.4 = 231.8
= 232mm

To obtain the metric size for dimensions over 60in, multiply the imperial size in inches by 25.4 and round to the nearest 10mm, taking 5mm upwards.

e.g. 67in x 25.4 = 1701.8
= 1700mm

About The Author

Jim Kingshott, born in the quiet Surrey country town of Godalming in 1931, is a professional cabinetmaker. He served his apprenticeship in the late 1940s, and over the last 45 years has gained experience by working in a variety of posts associated with the trade, ranging from undertaking to aircraft construction. He has also made a study of the history of woodworking, and the tools associated with it. In recent years, Jim has been involved with the training of apprentices. His contributions to various woodworking magazines in a freelance capacity have made him known to most serious woodworkers. When in the aircraft industry he was trained as a draughtsman, and this, together with a lifelong interest in photography, has made it possible for him to illustrate his writing in a unique way.

Index

OTHER TITLES AVAILABLE FROM
GMC PUBLICATIONS LTD
BOOKS

GMC Publications regularly produces new books on a wide range of woodworking and craft subjects, and an increasing number of specialist magazines, all available on subscription:

MAGAZINES

WOODCARVING   WOODTURNING   BUSINESSMATTERS

All these books and magazines are available through bookshops and newsagents, or may be ordered by post from the publishers at
166 High Street, Lewes, East Sussex BN7 1XU,
telephone (0273) 477374.

Credit card orders are accepted.
Please write or phone for the latest information